Barrelhouse

fiction. poetry.
pop flotsam.
cultural jetsam.

issue two
new fiction and poetry

ISSN 1555-7227

EDITORIAL

founding editors, fiction editors
Dave Housley
Mike Ingram
Joe Killiany
Aaron Pease

poetry editor
Gwydion Suilebhan

copy editor
Ilana Boivie

ART

art direction, book design
Anastasia Miller

photography
Kylos Brannon

BUSINESS MANAGER
Dan Brady

PRINTED BY
Signature Book Printing, Inc.
www.sbpbooks.com

For information about ordering, subscribing, or submitting to Barrelhouse, or to option Barrelhouse and the life stories of its editors for a Hollywood blockbuster or prime time soap opera:

visit our website at: www.barrelhousemag.com

or send an email to: webmaster@barrelhousemag.com

table of contents

DEAR READER,

We are totally punk rock.

What, you didn't notice?

That's okay, neither did we. Until, that is, we sat down to barrel-house around the old Barrelhouse with rock icon and entrepreneurial do-it-yourself legend Ian MacKaye of Dischord, Fugazi, and Minor Threat fame.

What does punk mean to you? we asked. And in a time when the word "punk" frequently appears in suspicious proximity to the words "Ashlee Simpson" and "Avril Lavingne," we'll take Ian MacKaye's word any day of the week.

Punk is "the free space. It's where new ideas can be presented. And it may not even be called punk—that's how free it is," he said.

And that's when it hit us. Holy shit, we might as well have green mohawks and safety pins coming out our cheeks. We are absolute, rock bottom, DIY fucking punks.

Of course we are doing this to present new ideas from different perspectives. Why else would we bring you fiction and poetry and essays on Barry Bonds, Godzilla, and convenience stores? Why else would we print a Very Special Swayze Section, like the one included in this issue?

Only because your friendly neighborhood punk rock literary magazine is all about providing an open space for creative people with something to say.

Besides, what's more punk than writing? What could be more do-it-yourself than creating something from absolutely nothing, with no resources but your brain and creativity and the blind stubborn arrogant courage it takes to turn a blank page into something as real and haunting as Matt Bell's "White Lines and Headlights," as funny/touching as Sean Beaudoin's "Rivals and Hyenas Alike," or as funny/thoughtful as Lee Klein's "All Aboard the Bloated Boat"?

As usual, our thanks go first to those talented and brave punks, the great writers who continue to submit their very best work to us, all of whom we are exceptionally proud to be publishing in this second issue of Barrelhouse.

There are many others to thank. New addition Dan "The Colonel" Brady, who as our business manager has inherited the unenviable task of inching us out of anarchy and into the black. Ilana Boivie, who copyedited every piece included here and created a style guide that told us how to handle TV shows, TV episodes, song titles, album titles, and anything else our pop-culture obsessed brains could throw at her. Anastasia Miller, who again created a brilliant design out of thin air (believe us, without her this journal would be a little too punk, like "scrawled in crayon on the backs of bar napkins" punk) And Kylos Brannon, whose photographs and artistic vision grace this issue, and whose own lurid genius meshes perfectly with that of Carrie Hill Wilner in the illustrated story "Sex and Pills."

We'll leave you with some encouraging words from an old punk, Johnny Cash:

> You've got to know your limitations. I don't know what your limitations are. I found out what mine were when I was twelve. I found out there weren't too many limitations when I did it my way.

We hope you enjoy what happens when we do it our way. We hope that like the great, departed Mr. Cash, we all find a way to walk whatever line we find ourselves walking. And as always, we hope you'll keep on barrelhousing, all night long.

All the best,

Aaron, Dave, Joe, and Mike

THE BARRELHOUSE EDITORS

:: by Matt Bell ::

White Lines and Headlights

I drive the second van, the one with the girlfriends. They're the most important part of the team, and nobody knows it but me. I do not know what happens in the other van, the one my sister Amy drives. Perhaps it is completely different, because it is the one with the actual team onboard and is believed to be the necessary vehicle. As for my van, it is full of girls and suitcases and plastic shopping bags. We are driving across a midwestern summer, ferrying a Japanese basketball team from city to city to play in goodwill games and all-star tournaments. My sister is the coach for the same reason she is found doing anything else—like me, she cannot say no. When she heard about this basketball team that was stranded, their coach dead of a heart attack at the age of fifty-three, she instantly jumped in. She met them for the first time at a memorial held for the coach in St. Louis, and I joined up a day later. She found me because I just happened to be living there at the time. When she showed up on the doorstep of the halfway house, I knew she wanted something. There was no other reason for her to visit.

Superficially I'm the assistant coach, but I wouldn't be here if Amy could have found anyone else to help her get these kids around. The previous assistant had been the coach's wife, and she flew home with his body. I stepped into her place and things continued. My sister and I, we've always fallen into one thing after another. She's an honor student at a university and a star basketball player at the end of her college career. I've dropped out of college only slightly fewer times than I've dropped out of the various clinics that have tried to cure me of my

I thought, Amy, remember when I lit your sixth-grade fair project on fire? Or when I told all the boys in school that you had herpes right before homecoming just because I didn't have a date?

problems. Different kinds of things, for sure, but accidents only look like accidents if you don't know the history behind them.

Amy stood at the bottom of the stairs leading up to my temporary porch, her All-American hands on her All-American hips. "I need you to help me."

I smoked a cigarette and stared at her. She'd only asked me for help once or twice before and I'd never been able to deliver. She said, "You'd have to come somewhere with me. For a couple of months. You'd have to be able to drive and that's about it."

When someone you're supposed to love asks for a favor, you tabulate all the ways you may or may not have failed them in the past. Ways you've wronged them that now mean you owe them. I thought, Amy, remember when I lit your sixth-grade science fair project on fire? Or when I told all the boys in school you had herpes right before homecoming just because I didn't have a date? Remember these things and others, maybe some I can't remember any more? Do you really want me to help you?

"You do still have a driver's license, right?"

I said I did, wishing that after all that time there was something better to say, but there wasn't. "I mean, I haven't driven in a while, but I'm pretty sure it's still valid."

"And you're clean this time, right? I mean, you have to be clean or this won't work."

"Of course. That's why I'm here."

"You have to be clean, Gary."

"I already told you I was."

"You have to really mean it this time."

I didn't protest again. It was like being caught at anything for the thousandth time. People kept asking you, but they were only willing to believe your excuses so far.

Amy drove us to the first game in a rented conversion van exactly like the one I'd be driving, paid for by a Japanese corporation. Karoushi, it was called, the word stamped on uniforms and duffel bags and matching t-shirts worn by the coaching staff. The old coach had worked for the company himself, and his wife was headed home to her widow's pension.

As for the basketball team, it didn't take long to see why Amy wanted to do this. We met the kids just before game time, but before running off Amy sent me to sit with the girlfriends, who looked at me with their wide eyes and didn't say anything. They scribbled in notebooks and after a while I forgot about them because the boys were incredible.

Physically, they were smaller than the other kids, but they were also quicker and had a kind of synergy I'd never seen before. The boy with the ball always knew where the next open teammate was. They passed more than necessary, often forgetting all about the basket. They effortlessly bounced the ball back and forth to each other and still scored enough to win all their games. I drove for the first time that day, the steering wheel an unfamiliar friend, getting me lost on the streets of a city I'd been in for six months but had never gone out into. Perhaps that's why I didn't notice how smug the girls were about the win, like little generals who've concocted victory after victory out of the most meager of soldiers.

Weeks later, we are parked outside a drugstore in Omaha, the hundredth such drugstore I've visited this summer. I've got the Big Book propped up on the steering wheel, reading by the streetlight filtering in the window. I'm shaking because I know what the girls are inside buying and also because I'm starving to death, having refused to eat anything the girls have prepared. They cook all of the team's meals and therefore mine. Amy takes her meals in conference rooms, meeting with other coaches and tournament organizers. She won't let me sneak away without the girls or the team because she's afraid I'll go get high, go get stoned. I won't eat for the same reason.

Amy thinks we're here to buy feminine products, but if the girls have ever bought tampons it was for some ingredient used in their manufacture.

A partial list of things the girls have bought: Dramamine, Sudafed, Nyquil, Tylenol Cold and Sinus, Robitussin, Mini-Thins, Tylenol, Aleve, Advil, sleeping pills, No-Doz, various gel caps in green and orange, always in green and orange. They buy iodine tincture and books of cheap store-brand matches and other things I never see but can probably guess at, if I really take the time to think about it.

The girls pile back into the van, all eight of them. I have to count heads because I can't tell them apart well enough to call roll. They all swap clothes every day and all have the same haircut. I wish they wore numbered jerseys like the boys so I could at least learn their numbers, if not their names.

They sit and talk in Japanese, too fast for me to pick up even the rudimentary words I've learned from them. They look into each other's plastic bags and point, laughing even though it's not funny. They're the kind of serious I remember well. As I turn on the engine and drive us back to the hotel I think of cooks bent over beakers and Bunsen burners and flammable liquids to be distilled into white powders, the kind that once set my spine on fire and made my brain free enough to forget.

The boys don't know what's going on, or at least I don't think they do. Still, could the girls have thought this up all by themselves? It seems ridiculous but I've seen a lot of crazy things that proved true later, when the lights came on. All I know is that some of the boys are losing coherence, showing static around the edges.

One of them, the starting point guard, Number Eleven, he looks at me across breakfast in Madison and says, "I had a dream last night." His English is the best on the team and so there's no mistaking him when he says, "You were standing in the road, staring at a pair of headlights coming at you. They got brighter and brighter, but you didn't move."

He looks dead at me and says, "You stood right there and got hit by a bus. Crazy." That's the team's favorite English word. Crazy game. Crazy shot. Crazy pass. Crazy dream. Crazy.

Number Eleven shrugs and looks back to the glossy brochures he's gotten from the college scouts who've seen him play. He's no longer grounded enough to understand what he's just told me. I'm frightened as bad as I've ever been, and that means a lot to someone like me.

When the boys play, it is with a gift that defies the intellects of other coaches, other players. They're athletes not junkies and so they don't know about precognizant experiences brought on by hallucinogens and amphetamines. I know all about these things and so I'll be terrified long after this trip is finished and these strange children are back in their own country. All I have to look forward to is the day Amy and I stand and wave goodbye to them as they board the plane back to Japan. It will be the first time I've been happy in years.

I sit in the suite's kitchenette, using the phone while the girls prepare lunch. I think about stories I've seen of Asian prowess in math and science and wonder how long before I find that ironic. On the phone is my sponsor, who wants to know how I'm handling myself out in the big bad world. "Temptation is everywhere, Gary. You've got to keep yourself safe."

"I'm doing well," I lie, turning my back to the girls so as not to watch them breaking up their assortment of pills. I can still hear the crunching, can still hear the sound of metal spoon clacking against the counter.

"Good to hear. You need anything, you call me, OK? You've got all my numbers? Work and home?"

"Right in my wallet."

"That's what I want to hear. Stay strong, brother."

"I will." I hang up the phone and put my head in my hands. The girls are all business, not talking as they cook. The only sounds are crushing and cutting, crushing and cutting. Rice fries on the stove and noodles boil in a pot and my stomach growls at the smell of the food

I'm not going to touch. I pick up the phone and dial my sponsor back. "Hey, sorry, it's me, Gary."

"Not a problem, buddy. You need something else?" He's happy to be of service. He's not scared, like me, but then what does he have to be scared of, safe in his home with his wife and his kids and his two meetings a day, every day?

I want to tell him what's going on, to say, this is crazy and I want to walk away but I can't. Not because of the team or these twisted girls or any of that. I can't walk away because I told Amy I would help her, and because I've done so many terrible things to her and to everyone else I've ever known. I've failed over and over and even though this is a bad trip I'll ride it just to know that I can do it. Just so Amy knows I can do it, because if someone else believed in me, I could too.

I want to tell him these things but don't, because I know he'd tell me he believed in me and that's not good enough. I say, "I just called to thank you again. For everything." I hang up before his cheerful response clears the receiver. The smell of food is overpowering, and I have to leave the suite. I satiate my hunger from a vending machine down the hall, stuffing my face while praying neither the girls nor Amy catches me away from my post. Hunger creates need and need makes me a junkie and that makes me want to vomit as I shovel stale potato chips into my mouth, hunched behind a hotel vending machine in Ohio. The next time I talk to my sponsor I will tell him, this is not an improvement.

It is hot and humid and the last week of August in Detroit. The boys are noticeably lighter than they were a month ago and Amy wonders about the strain from all the traveling. They eat like horses, she says. She doesn't understand why they're getting so thin. I tell her it doesn't matter. They're going home on Wednesday. I make a sad face so she can't see my relief. I don't want Amy to ask the questions because I don't want to give her the answers.

The boys win their first few games, which is no surprise. Still, there is something different. They look a bit slower, a bit weaker. Everything is taking its toll. Even the boys riding the bench are sweating. They drop the last game of the morning and go back to the hotel knowing that another loss will eliminate them from the tournament. This is their final chance to show America what they've got. The girls cook lunch with a renewed fervor, knowing that tonight's games are the most important of the whole trip. There are things at stake here, possible scholarships to good American schools for their boyfriends that could mean good American lives for them. Number Eleven's the only one with a real shot but the others are still hopeful. I sit and try to call my sponsor but can't get through. On the kitchen counter the girls chop lines the size of pinky fingers and add them to each boy's lunch. I gag and run into the bathroom. I stay there for a long time, and when I come out I leave the suite altogether.

Looking up at her, I can feel the tears in my eyes, can taste how rusty honest words are.

Just before game time Amy finds me in the stairwell, rocking back and forth, head in my hands. She sits down beside me on the steps. "What are you doing out here?"

I tell her I needed some time to think. She puts her hand on my shoulder and says, "You're doing really well, you know." She laughs. "To be honest, I can't believe how good you're doing. I was terrified that you'd ruin this for me."

Looking up at her, I can feel the tears in my eyes, can taste how rusty honest words are. "Amy, there's something I need to tell you. I've—"

She shushes me, her finger to my lips, and for a moment my eyes go wide because I think that she knows what's going on, that she condones it. Then she says, "You don't have to apologize, Gary. I know you're sorry. I'm sorry too, because maybe I wasn't there for you. We're making up for it right now though. We're doing something here, something good, and I couldn't have done it without you."

My stupid, merciful sister hugs me close, her arms wrapped around my ribs, and as I hug her back a tear does come, because I know I can't tell her what's happening. There are no words that won't ruin this, and I can't do that to her. I can't do that to me. I pat her back and stroke her hair and I finally remember that she really is just like me. She's built for good grades and scoring baskets and coaching kids. I smoke and drink and do lines of anything that can be chopped into a powder. It's just a small difference, and we're still empty without our fixes and I won't be the one who takes hers away. I know how much it hurts to have that torn from you.

They win and win, playing the best I've ever seen. The championship game begins with the girls surrounding me, clapping and laughing. There are no notebooks this time, no need to concoct new recipes in a swirl of measurements and equations. In the final seconds, Number Eleven goes up for the game-winning lay-up, leaping higher than his legs should physically be able to carry him. Up in the air his body jerks straight. The ball never reaches the basket, instead rolling off his fingers as he collapses to the floor. The ball bouncing away is the only noise in the arena as a seizure takes hold. The corporate logo emblazoned on his chest ripples with each spasm. Karoushi, it reads, and as I hit the floor running I know that he's going to die. They'll do an autopsy and believe that it's all my fault, this team of Goodwill Ambassadors laid low by a junkie van driver who fed them all pills. One look at the boys and one look at me is all it'll take to see the same haunted eyes, same gaunt faces, same extreme weight loss. The truth won't matter. Even I know that.

I leave without a word to anyone, without making eye contact with my sister. She screams my name behind me but I keep going. I know she won't follow me. She's too responsible. I flee the arena and go back to the hotel, where I take the Big Book out of my backpack to make room for the beginnings of a new stash paid for by my girls. It's the least they can do for all they've put me through, all they're about to make me endure. The first random handful of pills makes my stomach sick and my vision swims and as I drive away into the night all I can see are headlights. I drive faster until they blur together into one solid white line beside me, opposing me, coming straight at me. I press the pedal down and just drive. They will call it an accident, but only because they don't know the history behind it.

:: by Tom Williams ::

THREE-PIECE COMBO WITH DRINK

During the post-lunch lull at Cousin Luther's, I thought I discovered the cure to all that ailed me.

I was staring at the menu of that fried chicken franchise, trying to forget three form rejection letters, which had arrived that afternoon. Had the magazines been *The New Yorker, The Atlantic,* and *Paris Review,* I'd have been on my way to the Muscadine post office, but I'd been turned down by *Random Acts of Prose, Amateur Writers Unite!,* and an online number, *Boning the Muse.* With my fifty-first, -second, and -third rejections of the year behind me—and it was only mid-February—I preferred something stronger, but my Arkansas hometown was in a dry county and the package store fifteen miles away.

So I ordered a three-piece combo with drink. I filled my cup with ice and Coke, carried my tray to the restaurant's righthand corner, then sat with my back to the counter. I ate my sides first, the silken slaw and peerless dirty rice, and was simultaneously anticipating the first bite of chicken. Still, glimpses of the Xeroxed slips—none bigger than a matchbook—flickered on the edges of my mental vision, which recalled other rejections: from editors and agents, writing programs and conferences, for fellowships and grants. *Poets and Writers,* I feared, might turn down my subscription request. I believe I stood near a resolve then: Write one more piece of fiction and send it out. If it came back, I'd quit and learn to content myself as the night manager of the Delta Lanes Bowling Alley.

But at Cousin Luther's, it was time for the chicken. Not time to eat it yet—I needed a few more steps before I'd savor this fried chicken, mass-produced but still as fine as any southern granny's. I spread two napkins on my lap and splashed on my plate a puddle of Louisiana Hot Sauce. I tugged my chair closer, made sure I was the only patron—a person of color, I'm wary about public consumption of watermelon and fried chicken. And though it was perhaps my fiftieth visit to Muscadine's Cousin Luther's, I parted my lips as reverently as any choir member about to sing, then sank my teeth into the drumstick.

It was heavenly. As hot and spicy as my first bite had been years before. My eyes watered. Tears slid down my nose. I wanted to thank Cousin Luther (though he was a cartoon black man in a chef's outfit who resembled my Uncle Dobbs) and whichever of the high school dropouts in hairnets had overseen the pressure frying. This was no mere piece of poultry! After dunking it in my hot sauce, I took two bites of the leg, all the while moving toward a state of mind that I don't know if I'm glad I entered. As I tasted the chicken again, I believed something needed to be done to record how fine this three-piece combo with drink was. I turned to the cashiers and cooks, as glum a crew that minimum wage could produce. They needed praise, of a deathless sort, for their culinary achievements.

Brass plaques tarnish, sculptures crumble, paint fades. Prose fiction endures.

A work of art would show them, I thought. A story. Brass plaques tarnish, sculptures crumble, paint fades. Prose fiction endures. But could I write that story? Weren't there three pieces of evidence to cancel me out as he who might capture in a word or a thousand the splendid essence of Cousin Luther's fried chicken? Then, a new thought occurred to me: A story would be too brief. This three-piece combo with drink needed a novel to commemorate it. Had that been my proper form all along? Hadn't the editor of *Scouting Life,* in my one personal rejection note, told me my autobiographical tale of racial strife in a mid-South scout troop had the pace of a "longer work?"

I sucked the bone and my fingers, certain fate had brought me here for this moment of realization. Would it be three hundred pages? Four? I'd encountered no obstacles, though a pair hovered near: time and money. Did I have the endurance to labor alone at this task? No agent or editor had responded positively to my queries about proposed novels of biracial young men raised in the mid-South. I knew, as I cracked the drumette from the wing, I'd need at least three months without the bowling alley's distractions. How could I support myself? How would I buy more three-piece combos with drink! I didn't have enough in my savings, couldn't pawn my stereo and TV or sell my car to make rent, even at the cheapest of apartments. No friend or family member would help. My parents, cousins, even Trina, my last girlfriend, had advised me to give up my dream of seeing my smiling face on a book jacket. What to do?

After stripping meat from the wing with my teeth, I mopped my forehead with some napkins and closed my eyes. A patron. I could get a patron. Instantly, I saw myself standing next to Luther, both of us loose-limbed cartoons with bulging eyes, only my skin was two shades lighter. In his commercials, he often leapt and clicked his heels, while spouting, "So spicy it'll make your lips quiver!" But in my vision he handed me a check the size of those given golfers after winning championships. Then, as my mental cartoon continued, he uttered the restaurant's motto: "Go on and get you a good 'un at Cousin Luther's."

Soon I was soon placing the clean bones on my plate and hurrying toward the counter. The cashier I'd ordered from, a blinking, brown-skinned boy with a skimpy mustache, welcomed me again to Cousin Luther's, apparently having forgotten my earlier order. "I've already had a delicious meal," I said. "But I must speak to someone in charge."

"Follow me," the cashier said. He came out to my side of the counter, then led me past the restrooms to a door marked Private. He knocked. "Mr. Bartlett," he drawled. "Customer."

"Send them in," came a voice. The cashier blinked, opened the door, then left. Behind a sloppy desk sat a heavy-set white man with a crewcut, his short-sleeved shirt stretched across his chest, a striped blue tie loosened around his massive neck. "Was it frozen in the middle?" he said. "The rice hard? You can either get your money back now and our apologies for the inconvenience or a certificate for two free entrees under five dollars on your next visit." He banged open a drawer and rummaged within.

I said, "It's not that at all." I seated myself. "I've got this idea."

The manager closed the drawer. "You ain't here to complain?"

"Not in the least. Cousin Luther's is amazing! But what you need is a work of art, a novel, to show the world how lucky we are to have such chicken. And sides! Do you have a minute?"

Mr. Bartlett drew nearer and nodded. Or his neck spasmed. Either way, I told him how I hoped for the financial support of Cousin Luther's, Inc.—a nominal sum, peanuts, when one considered the potential revenue. He sat there, blinking as much as the cashier, and remained silent as I, with a rush of breath, said, "Don't you think that would be a great idea?"

His mouth opened, but for a long time he didn't speak. As I licked my lips—still sumptuous with grease—he said, "You'll have to talk to corporate."

"How do I get in touch with them?" I said.

He banged open the top drawer again. "Here," he said, thrusting at me an envelope with the address of their Little Rock headquarters. "I'm just the manager of 262," he said, and stood up to show me the door.

In my reverie I hadn't expected a lukewarm response. In my reverie I was communicating with a cartoon spokesperson. But Mr. Bartlett didn't cool the heat of my resolution. I ignored his snort and derisive call of "Good luck." At home, I wrote immediately my proposal to the corporate offices. As I figured on three months as the time I'd need, I requested five grand, roughly three months of salary from the bowling alley. What was that to them? I'd given Cousin Luther's that much money on my own! As well, I asked them how many millions they spent on commercials. They were getting my novel cheap! In my last paragraph, I advanced a notion—the only part of the letter worth quoting: "If the product of our relationship is fruitful, might not others follow Cousin Luther's lead? And will not that put your fine corporation in the vanguard, remembered as the fried chicken restaurant that brought literature to the masses?"

After printing it out and signing it, I stuffed the letter into the envelope given to me by Mr. Bartlett, then took it to the post office. Anticipation swelled with me—as it always did when I mailed a submission—but I felt no fear. Not once during the first twenty-four hours did I believe my idea would fail. But soon, despite my confidence, the only thing to do was wait.

In the interim, I went back to shelving balls and spraying shoes with disinfectant. I wanted to write but wouldn't let myself until I heard back from Cousin Luther's corporate office. I suppose I'd made up my mind that if they said no, I'd no longer trouble the world with my fiction. But nothing could dissuade me from my belief in the project and myself. Two weeks passed, then a third, while I clung to the writer's hope that the more time passes without word, the greater the chances success will result.

One thing I knew for certain about the novel was that it would be called *Three-Piece Combo with Drink*. On napkins and newspaper margins, I wrote this down, along with my name, as I'd read James Baldwin had while working on *Go Tell It on the Mountain*. For inspiration, I ate more three-piece combos. Daily, I ran to check the mail, often fantasizing whether the enclosed check required the corporate office to send its acceptance by UPS or FedEx. I spoke to no one about my plans, as friends and family had heard me describe previous stories and responded with either "Huh?" or "Why don't you just give that up?" Better to let them hear the good news, I decided, with the rest of the reading public—when the book was on the stands.

Then the day came when my mailbox contained more than circulars, bills, and donation requests from my alma mater, Arkansas State. I saw the envelope, cream-colored with Cousin Luther's smiling face on the left-hand corner. I couldn't tell by the weight of the envelope what the corporate office had enclosed. Giddy anticipation finally stepped aside, and fear, its shadowy companion, entered the scene. You've been delusional, I heard a voice say. Foolish. Wasting your time and that of a publicly traded company. A part of me hoped some coupons might be included with the kind but firm refusal.

But the sun was suddenly bright in my eyes, and the mid-March temperature too high to stand there waiting. I went inside, cleared my card table writing desk and laid the envelope down, seam side up. I considered a brief prayer, wondering if God loved writers so much He'd change the contents of an envelope if they promised enough contributions to charity. Yet He hadn't transformed any rejection slips during the hundred other times I invoked His favor. After several false starts, I opened it. The letterhead featured Cousin Luther's head too, with a cartoon bubble leaking from his lips and reading, "Go on and get you a good 'un!" I pressed the top of the page against the table and unfolded the middle third, whereupon I could see it had obviously been typed by a human being. I pushed down the bottom third, closed my eyes, let out a breath, and read.

I didn't know straight away what the letter meant. Only when I saw, "Contracts should arrive by courier as soon as we have verbal confirmation of your agreement," did I know I could retrieve my pens and pads. One might think I'd be overjoyed, dialing old girlfriends and English instructors who'd given me Cs. Surely a round trip to the county line package store was in order. But after I reread the letter, assuring myself Ms. Linda Parker was saying Cousin Luther's Inc. had, indeed, "found irresistible your idea and is earnestly looking forward to the final product," I called Mr. Dudley, my boss, to tell him I was quitting, then phoned the corporate offices and agreed to their terms. By the time I fell asleep at two a.m., I had written the first two chapters and was already dreaming of the third.

Some might have balked at this arrangement. A fried chicken restaurant's imprint is not the same as Knopf's or Simon & Shuster's...

Of all the time periods I've spent making up the story of my novel, this next was best. I wrote as one denied a pen for years. When the couriers arrived with the contracts—three days after I received the letter—I'd reached chapter six, some seventy-five pages of my best writing ever. I got three thousand instead of five, and two surprises: a laminated card ensuring me a year's worth of free meals (under eight dollars) from any Cousin Luther's in the continental United States, along with the guarantee that *Three-Piece Combo with Drink* would be published. I'd previously believed Cousin Luther's representatives would send the book to publishers; yet now I learned that, at their expense, Cousin Luther's was going to design, print, promote, and distribute the copies. Some might have balked at this arrangement. A fried chicken restaurant's imprint is not the same as Knopf's or Simon & Schuster's, sure, but the guarantee helped me write more swiftly. I'd known this would be a union of art and commerce. And if the book proved successful, who knew? Perhaps there'd be a sequel? McDonald's or Taco Bell might demand my services. Or my talents would gain the attention of traditional publishers and agents, and I'd be on my way to a career.

A reason for the ease with which I composed—twelve pages a day on average—was that my material was autobiographical. I made my first person narrator biracial—as I had with every other piece I'd written—although I moved his residence to Little Rock, a more appropriate setting for his occupation: sculpting. Never did I think long about making him a writer; that seemed corny. Plus, I didn't want my audience to think my creation and I were that much alike, though the plot possessed some parallels with my writing career. My character, Will, was more successful than I, but at the novel's opening, he'd reached a period of creative dissatisfaction. No longer able to summon inspiration, he longed for a return to the days when he hacked away at stone and shaped the figures his imagination commanded. I gave Will a love interest—though it was two years since my last date with Trina—to serve as a subplot: Will they marry? Also, Constance wanted him to give up his aesthetic pretensions and become more of a commercial artist.

Whenever my energy flagged, I reread the letter, especially the paragraph that concluded, "Your creative proposal assures us this novel is in the hands of an imaginative and skilled writer." Occasional daydreams befell me: I'd see myself dressed in a light-colored suit, before me an audience of adulatory readers. But I didn't take off one day from writing. I couldn't wait to read the previous day's work, where I'd often startle myself with the incomparable prose and dramatic plot moves. For instance, in chapter four, when Will eats his third three-piece combo with drink and realizes that this fried chicken—and sides!—should be the subject of his next piece, I knew all along I'd write that scene, but never would have guessed I'd write the line that ended that scene: "It was all very clear—the key to the lock in my mind had appeared in the form of a chicken wing." I set down the pen and left my apartment then. I could do no better.

And when I finished the draft and typed it into Microsoft Word— five marathon sessions of eighteen-hour days—I felt a slight sense of remorse. I knew I'd see the characters again—there were first draft details I was fuzzy on. Where did one purchase marble? Was marble even used by sculptors anymore? Even still, as I drove to Little Rock in my temperamental Ford Escort to hand over the draft to Linda Parker, I experienced the difficult task of sharing it with the world. I knew Cousin Luther's would be happy. In the three-hundred-twenty pages, I mentioned the restaurant two-hundred-nine times, Will and Constance ate there in six scenes, and Will ate there alone in five more. Four scenes featured him in his studio, eating chicken as he worked on his masterpiece—titled, like my novel, *Three-Piece Combo with Drink*. And with the climatic scene, where Will donates his sculpture to the corporate headquarters (a place I'd never been and hoped to visit for second draft corrections), I determined that Cousin Luther's had a book they couldn't have made better themselves.

My meeting with Linda Parker confirmed these feelings. In her airy, third-floor office (I'd made my version of the headquarters building too gray), she paged through my manuscript, remarking again and again on her pleasure. An intense and thin woman with odd glasses, she was not an Arkansan but a Chicagoan whose hard Midwestern nasality startled me. "Oh, that's perfect," she said one moment. Then: "Exactly what we wanted." She looked up from the pages and eyed me over the bridge of her glasses. "We haven't wasted a penny on you."

Before I headed back to Muscadine, Linda described to me the rest of the process while we ate three-piece combos with drink in celebration, and then she posed me next to a cardboard cutout of Cousin Luther for a publicity photo. There'd be a review of the manuscript by her PR staff, who'd suggest changes, then they'd approve my changes and pass the draft to the legal department, who'd make sure there were no libelous passages. (I had, in fact, made a few derogatory comments about KFC.) Then, definitely before August, the book would be out, and she and I would work tirelessly to promote it. When I stood outside the entrance to the building, ready to drive home, Linda shook my hand. Her grip was stronger than mine, and she wished me well. "Just wait," she said. "This is the beginning of a wonderful partnership." I wanted to hear more, but I'd already taken up two hours of her time and another meeting was calling her away. I had praise enough for the drive home. I could follow in my imagination the sequence of certain successes. Probably more than at any time, after those impossible years of what looked like failure from all directions, after, at last count, three-hundred-forty-seven rejections, along with dozens of manuscripts lost and dozens more returned unread, after all that, I believed I was a writer.

But no matter how ebullient I felt, it was the end of the period of creation. As soon as I put my pages in Linda Parker's hands, a new phase commenced. And when I got from her a call two weeks later that she was sending the corrected copy, I felt a pain in my chest. I'd done some research on sculptors and planned to make changes, yet I'd hoped my typed draft was immaculate, ready to go directly to bookstores. And, I was almost out of money. My taste for Cousin Luther's chicken hadn't ebbed—and they had a new catfish platter worth at least a short story—but I used my free meal card less and less.

Once I calmed down, I grew confident again. "Of course there were changes," I said to Linda. "Can't wait to see them."

"You did all the hard work," she said. "All we did was refine it."

"Thanks," I said.

"So let's get this puppy out in the world! All right! In time for late summer reading! And dining!"

Her excitement restored my confidence even more. When she hung up, I nearly ran to the mailbox. But I had another day at least to wait.

I tried not to predict what had been done with my draft in the hours I waited, but I couldn't quit thinking about the alterations. Essentially, I expected refinements, as Linda had suggested. A more accurate description of the corporate building. Perhaps some pruning of descriptive passages and a tightening of scenes. I wondered whom I'd be working with. Linda or another PR person? Though some resistance remained, I looked forward to the experience of working with an editor. To be truthful, I was also hoping for someone who wouldn't mind hearing some of my ideas for future work.

The corrected draft arrived two days after Linda's call.

There is a moment in many stories like the story of my novel where the artist finds himself the victim of unscrupulous managers, promoters, and executives but has no recourse. The contract he signed assures his hands are tied. This innocuous phrase tripped me up: "Cousin Luther's Incorporated assumes the full production of this work." I doubt any of Muscadine's personal-injury attorneys could have read that phrase and known Cousin Luther's intent. Even had I been warned, I wouldn't have done anything differently, as I believed this was the only way to see my book into print.

The title was the same, as was Will's ethnicity. (Linda told me: "He taps into both white and black demos.") And they kept him a Little Rock sculptor who donated his work in the end to the corporate office, though the point of view was switched to third person, a new crisis was added to the plot, and his medium changed to metal, which ensured a lot of noisy welding with flying sparks. Otherwise, *Three-Piece Combo with Drink* was unrecognizable. They'd made Will the manager of a Cousin Luther's on the west side of town, who sculpted in his free time. And, unlike a real manager, he actually ate the food prepared at his restaurant—at least once a day—often while commenting, "Damn, this is fine fried chicken! The best!" Constance was dropped, as a fiancée got in the way of Will's many demonstrations of virility (including a scene in which slaw and two biscuits serve as a means of arousal). Moreover, their Will needed far more energy than mine to fight off thinly disguised fast-food competitors, who schemed to acquire secret recipes and sent into Will's restaurant hordes of street brawlers, Ninjas, snipers, and finally a twenty-foot robot with laser beam eyes. The structure—a series of violent set pieces with bed-hopping and chicken-eating transitions—was execrable. The language, absurd. And anyone with an IQ over sixty would have sensed that no one who ate as much fried chicken as Will would have "arms of steel, legs of iron, and abs you could grate Cousin Luther's Chunky Fries with." The complete and utter badness of it would have made me laugh hysterically had the book not had my name on it.

I could have refused. I could have returned the money to buy back my draft and done with it what I wanted, taken out all the overtly commercial references and let it stand on its own as a novel of art, love, and fried chicken. But I may as well be plain in this account:

I didn't know if I'd ever get this close again. Not everyone writes *Catch-22* or *Invisible Man* the first time out! This was, let's say, my *Typee*, my *Fanshawe*. The next one—and I was convinced I'd write another—would make everyone forget *Three-Piece Combo with Drink*.

As for what happened after I signed off on all the changes, and Linda Parker said, "Aw'right," like one of Al Capone's henchmen, I wish I could forget. I wish I could forget the garish cover of a shirtless Will with a drumstick between his teeth, clinging to the robot's neck (whose wrecked robot corpse would become the raw material for Will's final sculpture). I wish I could forget the author photo—the very one of me and the cutout of Cousin Luther, in which it's difficult to tell who's more lifelike. I wish I could claim that all this was endured by another, but sadly I know all too well it was me.

A tour followed, with book signings and readings, but I didn't set foot in Borders, Brentano's, Square Books, or That Bookstore in Blytheville. Instead, in Memphis, Jackson, Hattiesburg, Fort Smith, Dallas, Monroe, St. Louis, and tiny truck-stop towns in between, I sat near the heat of open kitchens, signing grease-spattered copies, shaking hands with my audience (most of them quite charming, if illiterate), posing for photos with more cardboard cutouts of Cousin Luther, reading chapter excerpts over the hiss of the deep fryer and the squawk of the drive-thru speakers. As a courtesy, most managers suspended counter orders, though there was that angry manager in Grenada, Mississippi, a fellow mulatto who shouted he had too many orders to fill.

At every stop during those four months, I got reports from Linda Parker, so many that I started taking Benadryl before bed to muffle her blunt vowels echoing in my head. Cousin Luther's was doing quite well with my novel's release, bolstering its reputation among its existing clientele, luring bookish types, and earning praise from state and local agencies for promoting literacy. As I'd predicted, other chains tried to duplicate the success, the national ones chasing after King, Crichton, and Grisham, though no deals were ever made after my royalty arrangement—the sole mistake Cousin Luther's made as first-time publishers—was learned. If a nobody like me was getting twenty-five percent, many reasoned, the costs for an author of note would certainly eat most of the potential profit.

Meanwhile, I was selling more and more books, appearing on regional morning radio and TV shows. On one such appearance in Shreveport, the young Latina hostess asked me to read her "favorite passage"—a section where Will, in my estimation, cruelly victimizes a female spy from the KFC clone, General Sandy's Tennessee Fowl. I stumbled over the words and got lost twice, causing Ms. Rivas to say, "It sounds like you haven't read that before." Though this might have been the time to loudly proclaim the truth, I surprised myself with an awful equivocation: "Sometimes, when you're writing a book, it's as if someone else takes over." Then, before I forgot, I uttered what I was contractually obligated to say: "Go on, read you a good 'un at Cousin Luther's."

By the end of the tour, I looked horrible: bloated from so much fried chicken and sides, hollow eyed from lack of sleep, my fawn skin veering toward a jaundiced yellow. I showered five times a day but couldn't remove from my nostrils the stench of fried food. The suit I'd bought to match my dream was stained, sloppy, and unable to hold a crease. I was tired and felt older than my thirty-four years, but had one last appearance, in Muscadine, "home of my inspiration," according to Linda Parker. It was to be a huge occasion: all my friends and family—the harshest critics of my desire to write—promised to be there, as would be representatives from the press and Cousin Luther's, the mayor of Muscadine and the town council, along with Mr. Dudley, my former coworkers at Delta Lanes, and many bowlers who once rented shoes from me. After my limo ride to Franchise #262, I tried to smile and hoped only half of the people would want to buy me a three-piece combo "because you like them so much." Everyone greeted me at the door, Linda Parker leading the way. She grabbed me by the sleeve and, in the crush, scraped the side of my head with her glasses. Flashbulbs popped and sizzled, seemingly disembodied fists held aloft copies of the book. My parents were elbowed out of the way by Trina, whose last words to me had been, "I should never get involved with mixed nuts." Then #262's manager, Mr. Bartlett, resplendent in a short-sleeved shirt and a tie as wide as a dinner napkin, pulled my other arm and shouted, "I'm glad to have helped this writer achieve his goals." Even the kitchen crew and cashiers applauded then, all with a new paperback copy of my novel in reach.

Automatically, I did my act: read from the first and ninth chapters, answered a few questions, then signed books. My high school grammar teacher, Mrs. Ball, was thrilled I'd mastered the comma splice, and Uncle Dobbs—looking grayer than Cousin Luther but still nearly his double—wanted to know if the girl Will beds on page one-thirty-seven was modeled after a former Miss Black Muscadine. Then, after posing for more photos and choking down more three-piece combos with drink, I found an opportunity to escape. Everyone who'd ever known me was skirmishing to be interviewed by the just-arrived TV crew from Memphis, trying to say it was he or she who'd been the one who helped me out the most. I said my piece to the reporter, then excused myself to the restroom. While no one was looking, I ducked out the door. I stopped the driver of a Ford F-150, and he agreed to take me to my apartment, as it was on his way home. Once inside his cab, though, I saw skittering on the top of his dashboard a copy of *Three-Piece Combo with Drink*. The driver, an older white man with a John Deere cap, squinted at me, then we both looked at the book. He spat out the window, wiped his mouth, and said, "Ain't you that fellow?"

Even in my beleaguered state, I was too quick for him. Shaking my head, I said, "I get that all the time."

One pleasure of living in Arkansas is the many regions where a person can easily hide. With my money from the book—and there was a lot of it, I can't complain about that (save to say Cousin Luther's got even more, especially after they sold the movie rights)—I was able to rent this cabin in the Ozarks. I'm so far from the nearest dirt road that the only person who knows I'm here is my landlord, who doesn't have my real name and has only seen me with the beard I've grown to go along with my ball cap and dark glasses.

I came here not just to avoid the celebrity brought on by my novel. I wanted the self that authored *Three-Piece Combo with Drink* to disappear so a new one could emerge and write the fiction I want to be remembered for—instead of a novel whose greatest virtue is the two-for-one three-piece combo with drink coupon on the back page. My *Moby Dick* and *Scarlet Letter*, if you will. If I publish anything else, it will have to be under a pseudonym—an idea that came too late for the first book. Sadly, though, any identity I construct will face the same difficulties I encountered while laboring without success for so long. No wonder that in the sixteen months I've lived here I've not produced one page of fiction. Most days it is impossible to squeeze out a sentence. I started writing this very account with the hope I might stumble onto a new idea, but imagination comes harder and harder, as if by forgetting who I once was as a writer, I lost all connection to whatever talents I once had. Above all, I hoped a sober setting-down of that which occurred with *Three-Piece Combo with Drink* might once and for all silence the voice that seeks to continue in the vein of that book. But as I write these lines, a phantom taste spreads across my tongue, and even though the closest Cousin Luther's is miles away, I can sense the direction I need to take to get there.

:: by Paula Morris ::

LIKE A MEXICAN

The night I meet Carlos, I'm at the SoHo Grand with some of my colleagues after work. We're lolling on a low banquette when he walks in with Rico. They pull up chairs and order drinks.

Rico is an A&R scout working in our Mexico City branch, and he often comes up to New York to play us tapes. Tonight he's wearing the usual record company uniform of T-shirt and jeans. His friend, Carlos, wears a dark suit and tie. He looks about forty, older than the rest of us. Rico introduces me, says that I'm English, says that I work in International. Carlos, he says, is an old friend from Mexico City. He's a vice-president at a bank here in New York.

I barely speak to them at all. One of my colleagues has important gossip to tell me, information on political upheavals at the head office, on power-plays in Distribution. All we care about is work and vodka and hanging out at the SoHo Grand.

Rico and Carlos have to leave after one drink because they're meeting some other people for dinner and then going to hear a band. Carlos asks us if we'd like to come along.

"Maybe I'll see you later," I tell him, but I don't mean it. I've been living in New York for two years, and I'm used to keeping my social options open. I drink three martinis, eat some sticky marinated olives and a plate of cheese straws, and go home in a cab around nine o'clock. It's only Monday. I have to pace myself.

A few weeks later, I'm with a larger group of people at El Teddy's. We've just been to hear a German band playing at the Mercury Lounge.

It's a warm night, and the Mercury Lounge was stuffy and smoky, the floor sticky with spilled beer. At El Teddy's we can drink and eat chips and talk in loud voices while we wait for the food to arrive.

Mitchell, my boss, calls other people on his cell phone and tells them to join us. Before long, a tall, blonde woman in a black bustier turns up. She kisses Mitchell three times. She wants to know everybody's name and job title.

A chubby boy in a baseball cap shuffles in behind her. The blonde woman pushes him into the seat next to me.

"This," she says, staring at me with her wide crazy eyes, " is DJ Jeffy."

"Hey," says DJ Jeffy. He looks like the intern we just got for the summer.

"May I call you Jeff?" I ask him.

The blonde woman frowns at me.

"Order yourself a margarita, DJ Jeffy," she calls, walking off to the bathroom, arm-in-arm with Mitchell.

More people show up, and, by the time our food arrives, our party has spread to another two tables. Mitchell circles the groups, clapping people's shoulders, taking calls, making introductions. Rico walks up the stairs, and there's Carlos again, right behind him. He's not wearing a tie tonight.

Rico stops to talk to Mitchell, but Carlos comes straight over to me. He crouches next to my chair. I stop eating my burrito.

"Would you like to meet DJ Jeffy?" shouts the blonde woman. She's sitting on the other side of the table, blowing smoke rings in the shape of miniature haloes over Mitchell's head. Carlos ignores her.

"I was hoping you'd be here tonight," he says to me in a low voice. "I was hoping I'd see you again." There's something impatient about the way he speaks. His skin is lighter than Rico's, and he sounds more European. "I can't stay right now. But I wondered if you would have lunch with me. Perhaps next week?"

Carlos has stuffed his tie into his jacket pocket; a striped roll of silk bubbles out. He looks stocky in his suit. Even his head looks stocky.

His face is handsome in a stocky kind of way. I'm not sure if I want to have lunch with him or not. All I know about him is his name and his job and his place of origin.

"Just lunch," he says, smiling. His teeth are small and white. The smile changes him from stocky to debonair.

"Yes, well. OK." I smile back at him. He pulls out a business card and asks me for mine. We arrange to meet next week at Café de Lune on East 56th Street. I wish that Veronica Dietz from Corporate Communications wasn't sitting to my right, listening to every word of the conversation. I don't know why she's always invited to everything.

Carlos and Rico leave. Veronica Dietz winks at me.

"I think he's married," she whispers.

"Really?" I turn to my left. "Are you married, DJ Jeffy?"

DJ Jeffy can't speak. His mouth is stuffed full of food.

"I meant the Mexican," she says, scowling at the waiter telling everyone they have to smoke at the bar.

I catch a cab to Café de Lune, even though it would be almost as quick to walk. It's a warm day, and I don't want to arrive looking damp and out of breath. Carlos's invitation has made me feel singled out, glamorous, conceited. He's a Mexican banker who wears a suit to work and eats lunch in the East 50s: This makes him an international man of mystery. Everyone else I know is somehow involved in making or selling or promoting records. They got into the business because they wanted to wear denim to work and hang out in the studio with Bruce Springsteen or Quincy Jones.

I'm dressed in a shiny, low-cut blouse, a pencil skirt, and high heels. Everyone's been asking all morning if I have a job interview at another company. But it's a world away from Times Square here in the East 50s, and I'm the only person in the restaurant not wearing a suit.

Carlos is sitting at a table near the back, thrumming the rim of his glass. He's more attractive than I remember. He wants me to order the sea bass and have a glass of wine. He's charming and funny, and he wants to know everything about me.

My faces flushes, because I'm drinking red wine and talking about myself at lunchtime.

"You're English and you're beautiful, that's all I know," he says. "Tell me everything."

My faces flushes, because I'm drinking red wine and talking about myself at lunchtime.

Carlos's from Mexico City, and the bank he works for is a Mexican bank. He was transferred here a few months ago. He's known Rico all his life.

"You don't look like a Mexican," I tell him. "Not that I really know what Mexicans look like. Except for Benicio Del Toro, I guess. He's pretty cute."

"He's from Puerto Rico," says Carlos, smiling at me. "And I'm not really a Mexican, you know. Both my parents were born in Spain. So I'm Euro-trash, really. I hope you don't mind."

I was wrong about the way he looks: He's not square and stocky at all. He's almost a cartoon of a man, thick and muscular. Now I understand words like "virile" and "rugged." He's a dark, handsome, Euro-trash stranger from Mexico City.

"And you're married," I say.

"Yes." He doesn't seem surprised that I know.

"What does your wife think about you asking other women out to lunch?"

"Look," he says, brushing one hand over mine, like he's dusting a cobweb away. "My wife and I are separating."

"I'm sorry."

"She wants to have a child, and I don't. It's not a good situation, but we don't have to talk about it today. And please don't think I'm always asking women out to lunch. It's just—when I met you, I couldn't think about anything else. I kept asking Rico about you and wanting to see you again."

We leave the restaurant and he walks west with me, although he's told me that his office is in the opposite direction. We're passing a side doorway of the Plaza Hotel when he grabs my hand and pulls me up the steps.

"Come here," he says. He pins me against the wall and kisses me on the mouth. Around the mouth. In the mouth. It's one hell of a kiss—passionate, hungry, invasive. One minute we're walking along the street, the next we're suctioned to each other in a doorway. The kiss takes me by surprise and so does my response. I don't try to hold back or push him away. I lean into Carlos, arching my body up into his.

The kiss goes on and on, and I'm worried that the door's going to swing open, even though it looks sealed. I'm worried that some enraged doorman is going to jump out and hustle us back onto the sidewalk. I shut my eyes and try to forget things like doorway and public place and married man.

But then the kiss—this rude, flagrant kiss—ends. We're still in the doorway, and everyone is walking along the street not looking at us, like nothing's happened. Carlos says goodbye and stands on the stairs, watching me walk away.

I get back to the office feeling giddy and hot. I shut my office door and sit for a while in the armchair in the corner, trying to steady my breathing. My skin prickles. My heart is twinging and tap dancing. The kiss was better than records, better than drugs, better than vodka.

Mitchell barges in without knocking. He's wearing a Hawaiian shirt and waving a stubby cigar around. He wants to know if I've been over to Sony. Apparently, Veronica Dietz saw me walking in that direction.

I tell him that Veronica Dietz can go fuck herself: I had an appointment at the gynecologist's on Central Park South.

All I can think about right now are my sexual organs.

Several days and numerous telephone calls later, Carlos and I meet for dinner at Gotham.

He's waiting for me in the bar. We sit on high stools, close together. Carlos strokes my arm and the back of my neck. He tells me how desperate he is to see me. He tells me he thinks about me all the time.

Because Carlos's married, we can't pretend that this is like regular dating. And since the kiss in the Plaza doorway, it's too late to be coy or guarded. Carlos has his hand on my knee after the first drink; two drinks later, we're making out. Perhaps other people are looking at us: I don't know. I don't see anybody but Carlos. The waiter tells us our table is ready; we ask if we can stay in the bar.

I'm wearing a wrap-around dress that falls open a little when I sit down. Carlos draws his fingers up and down my inner thigh.

"The first night I met you, I could see your underwear every time you crossed your legs," he tells me. "It was driving me crazy. I remember, there were these little flowers over your panties. Gray flowers, maybe, or purple."

"I don't have any floral underwear," I tell him, but he doesn't believe me. "All my underwear is either black or white."

"I remember it exactly," he says, frowning. "Little flowers. Or maybe they were numbers?"

"You must be thinking of someone else." I drink the dregs of my martini. The twisting sliver of lemon brushes my lips.

"There's no one else," says Carlos. He sounds hurt. "There's only you." He gives me a broad, curvy smile, and I slump towards him, my tongue mashing into his tongue. He tastes like salt and cigarettes. It's the most delicious taste in the world. I want to lick his tongue dry. I want to eat the mouth off his face.

Carlos and I begin meeting up every few days. We choose bars where we won't bump into colleagues: Double Happiness, Milk and Honey, Flute. We drink too much and sit too close together. After three weeks, we've been out together eight times and had sex five of those times. We've had sex at my place. We've had sex in a Midtown hotel at lunchtime. We've had sex standing up in Mitchell's kitchen when we go there to feed his cats while he's away in Paris.

We talk obsessively about every time we've been out together, every conversation we've had, exactly what we were thinking at the SoHo Grand, at El Teddy's, at Café de Lune. We're greedy for each other. We talk, we laugh, we drink a lot. We like the Marx Brothers and anchovies. We don't like Pernod or the Dutch. We tell each other childhood stories. We argue about movies and books. He describes Mexico City and says he wants to take me there. I describe London, although he's already been.

We announce things: I miss you, I need you, I love you. It doesn't feel like an affair. It feels like we've invented each other. It feels like we've never been in love before.

Carlos's wife persuades him to visit a therapist on East 57th Street. They go together to the first session, but afterwards the therapist says she wants to see Carlos by himself.

"She asked me to stay behind for a minute," he says. He's calling me from his office, as usual. He calls at least three times a day. "She asked me if I was having an affair. I told her I was in love with an English woman, and she said she could tell."

"She could tell I was English?"

"She could tell I was in love with another woman."

He says he has to keep going to marriage counseling, even though he thinks it's a waste of time. He's not in love with his wife anymore, but he thinks that he owes her this much. He owes his family, too. When he got married to Valeria, the wedding was huge. Everyone rich and important in Mexico City was invited. Eight hundred people, six different bands. They even had fireworks. He's told me that his wife is the one with the money, but this is hard to believe. Carlos's parents have maids and a cook, and he says the staff still call him Master Carlitos.

"The wedding was a big deal," he says. "So it'll be a big deal if we get divorced. Everyone will be angry with me again."

I open my mouth to ask him what "again" means, but suddenly Mitchell's in my doorway, screaming at me to get to the conference room and watch the rough cut of a video. People are complaining that one of the dancers is too fat. The video was directed by Kenny Ortega; the fat dancer, it's rumored, is his cousin.

Mitchell is shouting that he only hired Kenny Ortega because of *Dirty Dancing* and because he was cheap.

"Can't we stretch her?" I ask.

"If we stretched her from here to Acapulco, she'd still look fat." Mitchell's face is so red it looks sunburned. "I don't want all of Kenny Ortega's fat fucking Mexican relations in the video!"

"You know, I think Kenny Ortega's from Palo Alto," I say, and tell Carlos that I'll call him back later.

When I do, he's been speaking to Rico. He's told Rico about our relationship. He's sworn Rico to secrecy.

Rico disapproves.

One evening, after we make love at my apartment, Carlos finishes getting dressed in the bathroom. He needs to look in the mirror to make sure his tie is straight. He's supposed to be at a business dinner.

"Remember when we had lunch together that first time?" he calls. I'm still lying in bed, the sheet taut around my waist. "I was so excited to see you again."

"So was I," I tell him. "Though I didn't really know what to expect. Not that kiss in the street, anyway."

"You looked so beautiful," he says. "Though I was disappointed when you walked in. I thought you would have dressed up more. I thought it meant you weren't interested in me."

"What are you talking about? I was dressed up!"

"I thought you would have worn something really special." He sounds petulant, as though I somehow betrayed him with my choice of outfit.

"I don't live in your world, you know," I tell him. "I don't work in bloody international finance. I don't go to balls every evening and polo matches every weekend. I can wear shorts and a bikini top to the office if I feel like it."

Carlos blows me a kiss from the bathroom door.

After he leaves, I run a hot bath and lie there with my eyes shut until the water turns lukewarm. I've never had such ferocious, athletic sex before. My tongue is tired. My stomach muscles hurt. Everything—my eyes, my teeth, my fingernails—are gritty and dry, except between my legs where it's sticky, pulverized. Even the hot bath can't quite balance my body.

When we see each other, it's like a round of a boxing match: short, intense, and violent. Carlos keeps saying that he's separating, but every week he's goes with his wife to see the therapist. He may have separated in his head, but his body is still married and living on 71st Street.

He worries about tell-tale stains on the pale green bed linen, but when I suggest he change the sheets, he looks at me like I'm crazy.

It turns out that Carlos's apartment is not only on 71st Street: It's just off Fifth Avenue. The only people I know who live that close to the park live on the West Side.

He and his wife are going home to Mexico City for the weekend, but she's leaving a day early. He wants me to come over that evening and see his place.

The building looks like it used to be some kind of grand residence or embassy. The floor in the lobby is marble; the curving staircase is ostentatiously wide. Carlos's apartment isn't especially big or especially light, but there's a subdued elegance to it. Everything's muted: books, paintings, furniture. The only strong color is the green of the park, visible through the bay window in the living room.

After we make love, we lie twisted together in bed, singing snatches of old standards. Carlos seems excited that I know so many old songs. When he sings "If I Loved You," I tell him he looks like Gordon MacRae. He smacks little-boy kisses all over my face.

He's not looking forward to going to Mexico City in the morning. The trip is Valeria's idea.

"She says she hates it here," he says. "She says we were happier at home."

He worries about tell-tale stains on the pale green bed linen, but when I suggest he change the sheets, he looks at me like I'm crazy.

"That would make her suspicious," he says. "She would see the sheets in the laundry hamper and ask questions."

"Why don't you just wash the sheets yourself?"

"I would never wash sheets. It would never enter my head that sheets need washing. She knows that. The housekeeper comes once a week; she washes the sheets."

"Well, what day does the housekeeper come?"

Carlos has no idea.

There's a small bathroom off the bedroom, and I walk in there to take a shower. It looks bare, as though all the soaps and bottles and lotions have been removed. The only thing hanging on the towel rail is a silky mushroom-colored bra. Valeria's bra.

It seems so delicate and limp drooping over the rail. Smaller and flimsier than anything I would wear, it's like a foreign object. She's left it here, unknowing, unseeing, to mark her territory. I look at it and suddenly Valeria is a person, real and vulnerable, reduced to this single insignificant detail.

I draw one finger down the skinny strap. She's probably a small person, as delicate and wispy as her mushroom-colored bra. She's dark-haired and petite, perhaps, gentle in her gestures. She has slender, expressive hands.

Maybe she looks slightly nervous or worried, which wouldn't be surprising: Her husband has persuaded her to move to New York, and she doesn't like it here. He says that he doesn't want to have children, that he thinks they should separate. She begs him to go to a marriage counselor, and even though he agrees, he's reluctant. It's only two years since their huge, expensive wedding, and he thinks that trying to save their marriage is a waste of time.

She doesn't even know the worst of it: that there's another woman in their home, having sex with her husband. A stranger standing naked in her bathroom, stroking her silky mushroom-colored bra.

I tell Carlos that I don't think I should stay the night, and he doesn't seem to mind. He has to get up at five to catch his flight. We both need some sleep. We've worn each other out.

Mitchell announces that he's tired of being out of the office all the time and that I have to pick up some of the slack. This means that he doesn't want to go to Vancouver or Los Angeles. Mitchell always gets tired of traveling when it doesn't involve Europe or Bangkok.

In Los Angeles, I meet up with Rico at the House of Blues. We're both there to hear a Mexican ska band. We go backstage afterwards to tell the band they were great. The band members are sweaty teenage boys, slumped in armchairs. They stand up to shake our hands. They can tell by the way their manager is behaving—jumpy, almost panting—that they need to make a good impression.

Rico and I go back to my hotel and sit outside by the pool. He shows me pictures of his two children. We order vodka martinis. I tell him that I love Carlos.

"No," he groans. "No, no, no. It's just an affair."

"A love affair, Rico. But I think we should stop—you know, for a while." I don't know why I'm saying this. Perhaps I want it to be true; perhaps I just want Rico to like me. "We can start seeing each other again when he and his wife separate."

"If," says Rico. He lights a cigarette and flicks the match onto the ground. "Look, forget Carlos. He's no good for you."

"You don't really believe that; he's your friend."

"I know him better than anyone, so you should listen to me. He's a fool."

"And I'm a fool, too. Just being here for a few days, I miss him terribly."

"Don't miss him," he says. "Forget him. He's a fool and he's a Mexican."

"You're a Mexican!"

"No." Rico shakes his head. "You know what Mexicans are like? Mexicans work in McDonald's."

I choke back a laugh and inhale a mouthful of vodka.

"I'm serious. Every time you think you miss Carlos, remember that. Mexicans work at McDonald's. Mexicans bus tables at restaurants. Mexicans clean hotel rooms. Mexicans sell oranges on the street.

Keep away from them."

"You're ridiculous."

"Listen to what I'm telling you. You don't want to fall in love with a Mexican."

"Whatever you say."

We clink our glasses and drink to not falling in love with Mexicans.

I get sick soon after my return from LA. I have the flu, and I feel too miserable to leave the house. Carlos says he's desperate to see me, so he comes over to my apartment.

When he rings the bell, I answer the door wearing my robe, a flaking tissue pressed to my nose. Carlos's standing in the hallway looking boyish and concerned, his arms around an absurd, towering bunch of red and pink roses.

Everything overwhelms me: the flowers, the sight of him, the aching in my joints. I leave the roses to soak in the sink, and we go to bed. I prop myself against the ridged board of his body. We stick together with sweat and saliva.

It seems like Rico's said nothing about our conversation in LA. Carlos's as ardent and desperate as ever. He tells me how much he loves me, right before he looks at his watch and says he has to go: Valeria has invited friends over to dinner, and he's going to be late.

His visit lasts barely over an hour.

The roses are beautiful. Their stems are two feet long. Nobody's ever given me this many roses before, not even Mitchell. He sent me two dozen after I procured a prostitute for Big Daddy V at the conference in Rome. Really, it was the concierge who got the prostitute, but I deserved the roses. I had to spend the rest of the conference with Big Daddy V following me around everywhere, asking me if he could get AIDS from a blow job.

When Carlos's roses begin to wither, I pluck off a few handfuls of petals and save them in a glass dish. Usually I hate potpourri, but I'm reluctant to let these roses go.

Carlos tells me we have to stop seeing each other for a while. Rico and his therapist are badgering him. He has to give his marriage a last chance. He has to make an effort.

We're sitting in a bar, as usual, after work. We're both drinking quickly, hurrying through the vodka and the conversation.

"I really have to," he says, moving coasters around the table with one finger. "I don't want to, but I have to try."

I nod, and try to act like I saw this coming, like I don't want to cry and throw my drink in his face and bash the ashtray against my head.

He has a story to tell me. Five years ago he was seeing a girl called Julietta. They'd been going out together for years. Her family knew his family, and everyone thought they'd get married. But Julietta was killed in a car accident. He didn't hear the news for almost two days, because nobody could find him. He was away, on the coast, with another woman.

"Everyone found out about it. Everyone knew," he says. "They were all angry with me. They were trying to arrange the funeral, but they couldn't find me. Finally Rico tracked me down. He told me what had happened."

Valeria, he explains, was Julietta's best friend.

"She was more angry than anyone else," he says. "She didn't want to forgive me. But eventually, we became friends again. And then we became more than friends. I think she felt sorry for me, in a way. Nobody could forget this bad thing I'd done. Nobody would forgive me."

"And that's why you got married?"

"People expected it. Our families, I mean. And I was thirty-four, thirty-five; it was time. We were good together, good friends. I thought I'd grown out of all this. Being in love. Passion. Romance." He gives me a rueful smile.

"Is that what it means to grow up?"

"I don't know." He peers into his glass, tilting the dregs from left to right. "I thought I'd settled down. Become a man, not Master Carlitos any more. But instead I feel guilty about Julietta and guilty about Valeria and guilty about you..."

"Don't feel guilty about me."

"But I do. I feel guilty all the time. There's something wrong with me: I'm not happy being married, and I'm not happy being in love. She's not happy, I'm not happy, you're not happy."

"You've made me happy," I say.

He leans forwards and grips my hands between his.

"Tell me you'll wait," he says. "I want to have children with you. Tell me you won't have children with anyone else. Promise me."

It's a ridiculous thing to promise, but he won't let me leave until I do. Then he pays the bill. We kiss goodbye in the street. I catch a cab home, feeling like shit.

It's three months since my first lunch date with Carlos. Only three months of a part-time relationship, a crummy affair. Still, I lie face-down on my bed weeping at the thought of never seeing him again. I feel miserable and sorry for myself. Several times over the next week, late at night, I call his voicemail at the office and listen to his message. I even write a poem. It's a bad poem. It says things like "streets littered with oblivious kisses" and "a summer scored with goodbyes." I keep it hidden in a book on my bedside table.

Months pass and my life shuffles back into humdrum order. Everything is the way it used to be: e-mails and meetings and business trips, interspersed with drinking and picking up the dry-cleaning. Carlos doesn't get in touch and I stop calling his voicemail at night. I try to avoid anything to do with Mexico, but Mexico is everywhere. Advertisements for Puerto Vallarta in a magazine, an interview with Jorge Rivero in the newspaper. A demonstration at the Mexican embassy on television. A new Mexican restaurant on the corner. A Frida Kahlo exhibition at MoMA. An Aztec exhibition at the Met. Bottles of tequila and Mexican flags everywhere I look.

Mexicans working in McDonald's, Mexicans bussing tables at restaurants.

In the New Year, everything changes. Rico argues with his boss and leaves the record company. Mitchell gets fired after Veronica Dietz complains to HR that he's harassing her. They've been having an S&M relationship at the office for months, and he became difficult when she tried to break it off.

And I get the chance to move back to London and work for another company. I'm tired of my job, I'm tired of New York, and there's nothing to keep me here. I'm happy to be leaving. There are almost no Mexicans in London. All the low-paid restaurant workers are European teenagers who need more money for nightclubbing and drugs.

The Friday night before I go, I stay up late to pack the last few boxes. I'm still padding around the apartment, brushing my teeth and looking for a magazine to read in bed, when the telephone rings. It's Carlos.

He says my name, and he sounds breathless, a little upset. I take the toothbrush out of my mouth.

"I just wanted to know that you're all right," he says.

"I'm all right." There's a coiling rope of anxiety in my belly. I feel sick and excited.

"I just wanted to know."

"Well, I'm moving back to London." I have to blurt it out, because I sense he's about to hang up. "Next week."

"Good, good."

"And you're all right?" I ask, because I want him to keep talking. I want to hear his voice. I want to hear his breathing, heavy and steady, at the other end of the line. He sounds like he's been drinking.

"Me? Yes. You're moving back to London, we're moving back to Mexico City."

"Oh." A glob of toothpaste drips from my mouth. I rub it into the carpet with my toe.

"So, you're all right," he says. "Every day I want to speak to you. So many times I've wanted to pick up the phone, just to hear your voice and know you're all right."

"I call you all the time," I say, but there's a click at the other end of the line. The conversation's over.

In the bathroom, I wash my mouth and sit on the edge of the tub, feeling dizzy. He probably called from home, and I have the number:

I could call him back, tell him I still want to have his children, still want to wait.

But I don't call him back, because he's married to someone else. I'm moving back to London, the place I belong, and he's moving back to Mexico City, the place he belongs, the place where he was married in front of hundreds of people, hundreds of witnesses, hundreds of affluent, well-dressed, well-spoken Mexicans. Carlos did something bad: He was caught carrying on with another woman while his girlfriend lay dying. But everyone had forgiven him, and he married his girlfriend's best friend. There were six different bands. There were fireworks. It was a wedding and an atonement.

If the story about Julietta is true.

That weekend, packing up the last of my stuff, I throw the poem away. I tip the rose petal potpourri into the trash. When I get to London, I buy a new address book and decide not to copy Carlos's telephone number into it.

In London, my life is quite different. I don't work so late in the office. I don't go out so much afterwards. Cocktails are too expensive, so I switch to white wine. Cabs are too expensive to catch all the time, so I get a monthly rail pass. Soon I'm drinking much less, and getting to bed at a reasonable hour. I don't eat olives and cheese straws for dinner any more. My new friends have names like Emma and Kate. I never hang out with guys called DJ Jeffy.

People invite me to dinner parties. On Sundays, I start going to Battersea Park with my friends to rent row boats, or to the local Portuguese café for fish cakes and coffee. This is a new kind of life for me. I'm getting old and respectable. I only go out with single men.

Late in the summer I meet a man named James at a barbecue. He's a tall, good-looking barrister, and all my friends are envious. He takes me out to dinner, to the theater. We go away for weekends to Brighton and Rye. After six months, we're a real couple. We host dinner parties together at my house and watch films together on his big-screen TV. We stay in.

I hardly think of Carlos at all. One day I realize that I can't remember his last name.

After a year of dating, James tells me that he wants us to move in together. He says it will save time and money. If I give up my place and move into his flat, I'll only need a two-zone travel card. We can sell all our duplicate CDs and merge our DVD collections. At some hazy point in the future, we can get married in a marquee on my aunt's lawn. We can invite all our friends. We can serve Pimms and a cake made out of profiteroles, and we can honeymoon in Madeira or Dubrovnik, whichever I prefer.

We can have children.

Although I'm very fond of James, I don't want to live with him or marry him or merge with him in any way. We don't love each other enough. We have sex the way some people eat dessert: occasionally and furtively, as a special treat. I don't want a big wedding to feel guilty about when we sit there in marriage counseling two years later, wondering what the hell went wrong.

When I tell him this, he looks sad but relieved. There isn't a scene of any sort, because James isn't one for scenes. James is English. He's stoic and understated. He kisses me on the cheek and wishes me all the best. It takes him several goes to maneuver out of his parking space. I stand in the doorway of my house, wondering if I should wave or not.

After a few weeks, my friend Emma calls. James has asked her out to dinner, and she'd like to go. She wants to know if I mind.

I tell her that I don't mind at all.

On a drizzly day, two years after I move back to London, I'm in the back of a taxi driving along the Hammersmith flyover.

The last time I saw Carlos, we said goodbye outside the bar, standing under a tree twisted with fairy-lights. We clung to each other, stuck like glue. He kissed me, and the sensation of his mouth on mine, his face so close, made me feel intensely happy and desperate at the same time. Our last kiss was soft and slow, not at all like that insolent first kiss in the side doorway of the Plaza Hotel. We'd had three months of afternoons and evenings, love and talk, and this was where it ended—in the street, Carlos standing on the sidewalk and watching my taxi drive away.

The sky was dark blue and empty, unfurling like a long ribbon above our heads. It felt like the end of the summer. I gazed back at him through the grubby back window of the cab. He was standing, still and crumpled, on the curb. Both our faces were turned towards the place we last stood together.

Today I'm just looking out the window at nothing in particular, watching the rain dribble down the glass. The taxi drives past a huge billboard advertising tequila. There's a picture of a grinning man wearing a sombrero and holding a giant bottle, its label painted the colors of the Mexican flag. A bubble as big as a swimming pool reads: "The real taste of Mexico."

The brown-skinned man on the billboard looks happy. He's probably just been to a big wedding, and heard a lot of music, and seen a lot of fireworks. Perhaps he's just met some silly girl and thinks he can see little flowers all over her underwear. Perhaps he knows that some day a reckless, love-drunk foreigner will sit with him in a bar and promise to bear his children.

So I smile up at him and blow him a kiss. He looks like he works in McDonald's. He looks like he sells oranges on the street.

:: by Lee Klein ::

All Aboard the Bloated Boat: Arguments in Favor of Barry Bonds

On July 6, 2005, Girlfriend and I drove to Fairfield, Iowa, home of the Maharishi University of Management (mum.edu), a business/ spirituality school led by His Holiness Maharishi Mahesh Yogi. A distinctly Vedic-flavored Midwestern town, Fairfield is famous for rumors of rampant levitation among its citizenry—a significant thematic fact, considering that this essay's final sentences offer some thoughts about transcendence in a fucked-up world. Please realize the following isn't about rampantly levitating new-age freaks in Fairfield, Iowa, however; it's more about the ocean of corn (and maybe an iceberg lurking somewhere in it?) we saw when we drove to Fairfield two days ago. You know the old saying about how the corn's knee high by the Fourth of July? Well, as we drove through southeast Iowa to see the levitators of Fairfield, we passed not much knee-high corn, a whole lot of the eye-high stuff, and a handful of cornstalks so impressive you wanted to uproot one, take it home, and hang a basketball hoop from it.

The sight of sky-high cornstalks made Girlfriend say: "No wonder nine-year-olds menstruate these days."

To which I replied: "Huh?"

"All the hormones in food," she said. "They hit puberty when they're like nine."

This exchange inspired what I thought might be the first line of an essay I'd been gearing up to write for months: If Barry Bonds were a vegetable, he'd be the biggest, reddest, juiciest tomato that ever made your daughter bleed before her time.

BONDS

Much is made of steroid use by home-run hitters. People say their records are tainted. People say these guys are terrible role models. People say they're cheaters. And yet, in ever-earnest Iowa, the corn is sky-high two days after a birthday celebration for a country in which televisions are now how many inches wide? XXXL is not so uncommon a size. Instead of Mustang, Pinto, Bug, or Beetle, today's enormous cars are called Sequoia, Tundra, Rainier, and Yukon (not to mention the environmentally evocative Avalanche). Our armed forces' capabilities to kill, often while miles out of retaliation's reach, seem downright Atari-an, if not PlayStation2-ian. Our meal portions are famously super-sized, occasionally complemented with vegetables that make children hit puberty before they can spell menstruate. And who best personifies all this?

Barry Bonds, of course, he who grew up around the professional game. Whose father (Bobby) and godfather (Willie Mays) are baseball legends. Who worked hard. Who excelled at every level he played. Who at age thirty-seven hit seventy-three homers in one year and seemed on track to shatter Henry Aaron's career home-run record. Except he was on steroids, supposedly. You know all this. No need to waste words. But the thing to think about when you think about the effect steroids may have had on Barry Bonds, I think, is that, from Little League to last year's season, he's always been one of the best, if not *the* best.

Imagine you, like me, know what it's like to be one of the best Little Leaguers. Imagine you know what it's like to take the mound and win a high school state championship. Imagine you know what it's like to strike out fourteen in a twenty-one-out college game against the number-ten-ranked Division-III team in the country. Imagine you know what it's like to dominate. Imagine you excelled at pitching for thirteen years, but you didn't take your game to the next level: didn't spend your spare time lifting and running and throwing weighted balls to increase your heater's speed seven measly miles per hour so it'd hit ninety on the radar gun. When you threw a slider at a righty's head, the batter bailed in fear, called out on strikes as the ball cut across the zone. When you threw a curve, it looped so high and dropped so quickly field umps often said "wow" as they tipped the pointy brims of their tiny black caps. When you threw a forkball, it tumbled and fell without much rotation, sometimes skidding unpredictably like a knuckleball. But your fastball—your eighty-three-mile-per-hour heater—college kids caught up with. It was more than fast enough in high school. But not in college, not even in Division III.

Faced with college-level competition, you didn't work harder on and off the field. You definitely didn't live in the weight room. You, like everyone you've ever played with, didn't do what Barry Bonds did. Instead, just like everyone you've ever played with, your interest switched to something else. In my case, that something was guitar. Barry Bonds, meanwhile, committed himself to transforming his natural baseball talent into something almost scary. And it was this drive to be baseball's best—not just of his era, but of all-time—that may have compelled him to take a legal substance widely used by power hitters and pitchers alike, through which he began to compete more with history than with contemporaries who, like the timid bitches they were, once walked him 232 times in one season; he was that good.

And being that good made people who could never play baseball well in Little League, let alone the high school, college, or professional levels—let alone fucking drunken games of Wiffle Ball!—question an ability that seemed to raise the bar high over the head of even the greatest hitters of old. Forget that The Babe hit in a stadium known as "The House that Ruth Built," famous for its short porch in right over which he hit many a home run. Babe Ruth lived on hot dogs and beer, not steroids, so it's okay—or so people say. Having a stadium built to your advantage is not cheating.

Further, how many of Bonds' home runs just barely cleared the fence? Mostly they were towering shots into the water over the bleachers in right. Home runs anywhere. And how many homers would he have hit? Pitchers never came close to throwing him strikes, so intimidated they were by his stroke, which was not built on steroids alone: Bonds worked out one winter with David Eckstein because Barry admired the pesky infielder's bat speed....

ENOUGH THEORY, LET'S PRACTICE:

Try this at home: (1) sniff out the cell phone number of your neighborhood's performance-enhancing drug dealer; (2) shoot some steroids into your limp white office-worker limbs; (3) go stand in the batter's box as some lanky twenty-five-year-old Dominican, Venezuelan, or Texan, out of his mind on amphetamines, cranks ninety-five-mile-per-hour heaters high and tight; and (4) try touching one of these pitches, motherfucker. C'mon, let's see you get some wood on an eighty-seven-mile-per-hour changeup. Let's see your steroid-addled ass play in front of tens of thousands of people every day every summer for a dozen years while wearing clingy pinstriped pants completed with cute little elastic stirrups.

Before you find that cell phone number, imagine for a second all the work it'd take to go from watching your fantasy baseball stat tracker and popping your steroids to hitting a ball into the water over the right-field bleachers and trotting around the bases just once in real life. (Bonds currently has 703 home runs.) Imagine all the work it'd take just to hit one out. Imagine going back in time to when you were six. Imagine hanging all day with Willie Mays (often considered the best of the best) and Bobby Bonds (not to mention your dad's teammates like Willie McCovey and Don Baylor), these guys giving you hitting tips long before you knew how to spell the word cheating. Imagine every pitch you crushed from age seven onward. Imagine all the time in the weight room. All the time running. All the time studying pitchers. All the time denying indulgences because it's baseball season. Imagine all the flights around the country. Imagine all the home runs.

All the cheers. Imagine all this happening before you decide to take some hormonal supplement to make it easier to work out, harder to compensate for natural aging processes. Imagine the confidence you'd have knowing how well you're working out these days, thanks to the juice. Imagine the swagger. Imagine standing in the batter's box, your arm (usually exposed to the bean balls scared pitchers throw in self-defense) now covered in gladiator-like armor. Just imagine what it'd be like to play the game for two decades before you ever took any sort of hormonal enhancement....

Now imagine everyone turning on you. Writing off all those years of work that enhanced your natural talent. Writing you off because you took a drug late in your career that helped you work harder and perform better. A drug the pitchers took, too. Imagine they make you the poster boy for steroids, citing the obvious symptom of the long ball, while half the people bitching are on antidepressant pills. While Roger Clemens and Curt Schilling slide by unnoticed, these huge, aging, aggressive strikeout pitchers who you just know are juiced. While a steroid-addled Rafael Fucking Palmiero cashes in on his 500 home runs by appearing in ads for Viagra ($4,000 of which he donated to George W's reelection campaign, by the way). While you spurn the bullshit posturing required to win endorsements. No different from Ted Williams, controversy has always fueled your performance. You thrive when it's you against the world, and so you bark at the media, say crazy shit, and antagonize your teammates, just so it'll spur you on to win. You fight with everyone to improve your game. Everything you do you do to make your game better.

And that's your fatal flaw. All those years of work, all those batting tips from Mays, Stargell, Parker, etc., the seven MVPs, the eight Gold Gloves, the thirteen All-Star games, the thirteen consecutive years hitting thirty or more homers, the single-season on-base percentage record of .609 (!), being the all-time leader in walks (holding the single-season record for walks with 232 [my god!], as well as the record for intentional walks with 120), not to mention hitting seventy-three homers in a season and being one of only three human beings ever to hit more than 700 homers in their careers—all these records and awards and years of commitment to the game mean absolutely freakin' nothing because you, like everyone else in the league at the time, it seemed, took what was available to make yourself better. And since you were already better than everyone, it made you better than anyone ever, and that didn't sit well with some people who envied what you could do. The drive that got you where you are destroyed your reputation. Similar ambition has caused the fall of empires.

Sky-High

But, hey, it's not like you're Dock Ellis, who in the early '70s threw a no-hitter on acid, who also took a handful of uppers every time he hit the mound, like so many others. You weren't tripping out there. You were working. In fact, you were a lot like this little black boy from the Pacific Northwest who loved his guitar so much he slept with it, who played and played, who spent most of his time in the Air Force playing guitar, who traveled all around the South playing guitar, who played rhythm guitar for the Isley Brothers and Little Richard, who played in New York in the mid-'60s under the name Jimmy James—until certain performance-enhancing drugs entered the scene. And all that talent and all that work met all those drugs, transforming Jimmy James into the most exciting guitar player Brian Jones of The Stones had ever heard, or so he said when he introduced the relatively unknown Jimi at the Monterey Pop Festival in 1967. Ever hear the rumor that Hendrix sliced his forehead with a razor blade, then pressed tabs of acid into the slit, then tied it down with a headscarf so the hallucinogen seeped directly into his brain as he played? Ever hear Jimi's rhythm playing on "Wait Till Tomorrow"? Ever hear the bombs dropping toward the end of "Machine Gun" on the *Band of Gypsys* album?

The comparison between Bonds and Jimi is clear: natural talent + obsessive work/play + performance-enhancing drugs = godlike greatness.

In both cases, it wasn't just the acid or the steroids that created the legend. The equation is much more complicated than just simple addition involving drugs. Mind-blowing performance was founded on sleeping with baseball bats and guitars, years of obsessive practice, tons of natural talent, and then (and only then), the drugs.

Think of The Beatles before *Rubber Soul*. Myth has it that Dylan intervened, performing two of the most important miracles in the history of rock: (1) "Why are you guys singing that 'love me do' crap," he supposedly said, "You're too good for that;" and (2) he introduced the mop-headed musicians to weed. What came next? "Norwegian Wood" on *Rubber Soul*. And after that: *Revolver*, which (like Bonds and Jimi) some call the greatest. Which reminds me of Bill Hicks' stand-up routine about "the war on drugs," how all great music was played by people on drugs, and so if you're against drugs, the first thing you should do is take all those great albums by The Beatles and The Stones and burn them, because they were all made while everyone involved was "real high on drugs."

Like Bonds, I played baseball. And like Jimi and The Beatles and The Stones, years ago I played a lot of music while "real high on drugs." But the drugs didn't transform what natural talent I had into something special. Most likely, steroids wouldn't have helped my pitching much either.

So where does that leave us?

BOMBS

Right after I typed that question, I got an Instant Message from a friend in London:

friend: p.s. i'm alive
me: huh
friend: seen the news?
me: you won the olympics bid!
friend: are you joking?
friend: did you just wake up?
me: i just checked nyt.com
me: shit
friend: right
friend: six bombs

friend: and a scare in my street
me: shit
friend: just got back in the house
friend: it ain't 3000 people, but we're scared
friend: they think about 50 or so dead
friend: about a 1000 injured
friend: some critically
friend: we've been waiting for ages and now it's here
me: i'm reading this now - the tube - damn
friend: yeah

Tragedy so weirdly appeared when I was paused after that Hendrix/Beatles-on-drugs rant, trying to figure out how to steer the argument toward the bigger picture. And, lo, an eerie segue appeared to provide the following simple idea: Who the fuck cares if some idiot kid is influenced to take steroids to make his fastball hit the nineties when this idiot kid lives in a world where idiots try to enhance their ideological performance with explosives, whether it be the bad guy's makeshift sack of dynamite on a double-decker bus or the good guy's million-dollar missiles jettisoned from miles away as though playing some "graphically rich" evolution of Atari's Defender. (Make no mention of the good guy's weapons of mass destruction set to destroy all life on the planet how many hundreds of times over was it again?)

I swear there's a connection here. I swear there's something that makes steroid use acceptable as an evil so lesser it's comparatively angelic. I swear Barry Bonds is a scapegoat for larger troubles. Compare with any sort of warfare the significance of Barry Bonds juicing himself—like Robert Johnson selling his soul to the Devil so he can play guitar better than no one's ever done before—so baseball fans around the country can come away from a game saying those inflated ticket prices were worth it to see Bonds hit a 500-foot moon shot. Compare steroid use with "Shock & Awe" in Afghanistan and Iraq, with Al-Qaeda's actions in New York, Washington, Madrid, and now London. Imagine you've been orphaned by an American missile. Imagine you've consequently developed a hatred for the United States, a hatred you sleep with every night. You work at that hatred, plan to unleash that hatred, and then there's an opportunity to get your filled-with-hatred hands on something abstractly analogous to performance-enhancing drugs: Instead of Barry Bonds with steroids and a mighty baseball bat in his hands, imagine you're some anonymous terrorist with Uranium and a mighty hatred of America in his heart. The wonder of the bombings in London and Madrid is that both have been surprisingly rinky-dink compared to the expectation of an atomic blast.

The inevitability of a devastating urban strike has nothing directly to do with Barry Bonds's steroid-addled assault on the home-run record. But tainted homers, I think, are a sliver of something more invasive, if only in that we focus on over-inflated home-run records because the scandal distracts from the over-inflation of American bodies, the over-inflation of houses, the over-inflation of cars, the over-inflation of our armed forces' capabilities, the over-inflation of patriotic self-importance, the over-inflation of self-righteous, nationalistic cluelessness, the over-inflation of a sort of laziness that makes you think you can get results without any effort (that makes people think baseball players simply stand at the plate on steroids and hit homers without the physical memory of two dozen years of effort and experience having anything at all to do with how far the ball soars), and, finally, of course, we focus on over-inflated home-run hitters instead of the over-inflation of performance-enhanced produce that makes our daughters' bodies mature way before their prime.

But what about their minds?

Here's where I offer some final thoughts about transcendence in a fucked-up world, a world in which joys as simple as the home run, the corn cob, and the tomato are tainted. Why do we question the long ball more than international difficulties caused by an out-of-control addiction to oil that makes us a sedentary society that drives to fast-food chains and then wants pharmaceutical companies to offer obesity pills that don't make us shit our pants? Why do we holler about some naturally gifted, hard-working athlete's semi-unnatural ability to hit a baseball hundreds of feet over a fence when a simple foot would do? How might one transcend the hypocrisy of booing Bonds when his homers are no more bloated than most everything else? Maybe by driving to weird places like Fairfield, Iowa, where no Al-Qaeda member would ever think to strike, where the drug of choice is surely crystal meth (or Maharishi mind warp), where a hot-air balloon hung over town as we walked around the gazebo, on which leaned a lonely saxophonist, who sent overly enlightened licks into the summer air, and where the Thai food was really fucking remarkably good.

What I mean to say is that, like in Fairfield, Iowa—where so many fliers for transcendental-meditation sessions hang around the traditional midwestern town square—maybe the only way to transcend the hypocrisy is to expect your home-run hitters to take performance-enhancing drugs, sort of like tribal shamans reflecting the current state of the world. If everything's naturalness can be questioned, please don't deride one man's ability for doing something as pleasurable and benign as hitting dingers—unless you're consciously singling out Bonds & Friends because you believe sports are an alternate reality where steroids stand for everything in the world that's wrong, that you'd like changed, but don't have a clue where to start. But if you see steroids in baseball as part of a whole in which even the tomatoes are juiced, maybe it's better if puberty begins when kids are no older than ten. Maybe a head start on the maturation process will make it easier to realize that steroids are not even the tip of that icy impediment up ahead of our unnaturally bloated American boat.

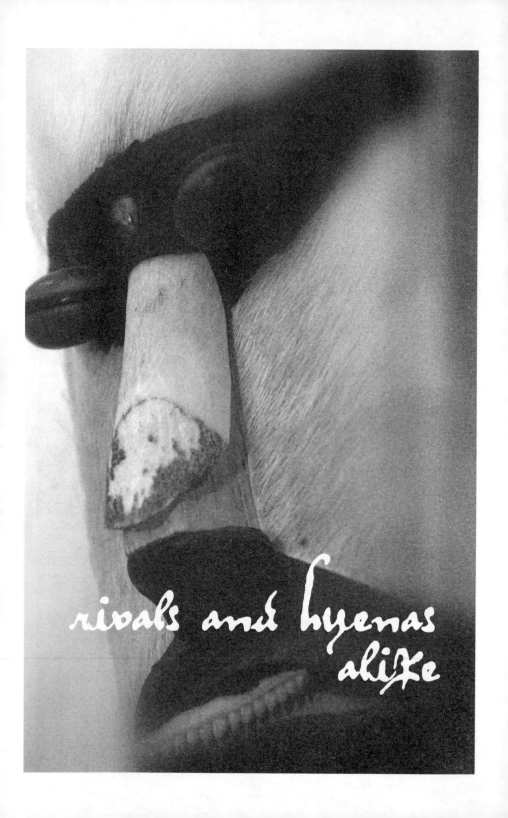

rivals and hyenas
alike

:: by Sean Beaudoin ::

I was unemployed but not jobless. The Basement was at the top of a list taped to the refrigerator.

"Get rid of everything," my father said, stepping into the kitchen. He was barefoot. The linoleum was cold. "Except the rakes."

Our lawn was an apron of poured concrete. Wire fence enclosed a long-dead oak that would never shed a single leaf.

"We have rakes?"

"Let's go." He said, making a chopping motion with his hand, "Chop chop."

I followed a lone Corn Puff with my spoon. Milk parted in tiny wavelets and met again in the center of the bowl.

"I'm not finished."

Sometimes stalling worked. My father tended to be aggressive in the mornings but usually gave way to a general dodder by noon.

"You were finished before you started," he told me, and then blew his gym-teacher whistle. It was metal and hung around his neck and made an annoying twee that hurt my ears.

"Don't."

He stood with his arms crossed, legs wide, a knobby stance that said, Assistant Linebackers Coach. It said, You're this close to laps.

I trapped the last Puff like a minnow, stabbing into the bowl with two fingers. Then I ate it. There was milk on my chin and my shirt and the table.

"Finished?" he asked, checking the spot on his wrist where a watch might have been.

I put my bowl in the sink. There were a stack of bowls already there. The dishwasher was full of bowls, and so were the cabinets. My father refused to eat anything off a plate.

"Finished." I told him.

"Good man," he said, and then pinched my deltoid. "Teamwork."

I swept the floor and then hosed the corners. I moved the rakes. I carried a pile of cardboard to the far wall, and then re-stacked it, throwing away exactly nothing. It had all been my mother's.

"How's it coming down there?"

My father's shadow fell brokenly over the stairs, not quite reaching the concrete. He refused to enter the basement, ever.

"Come see," I goaded.

He cleared his throat.

"C'mon down. It looks great."

He shuffled his feet and then turned the doorknob, fast, ratcheting it back and forth.

"Well?"

"Just finish, that's all," he said, and then closed the door.

I decided to tackle a pile of crates behind the water heater. The first few were light and empty, and I threw them as far as I could. They tumbled end over end, making a satisfying racket. The third was heavy and hurt my back, so I let go. It broke open, like an egg.

And there was Zulu, staring up at me.

He was about a foot high, nestled among pictures and broken watches and a moldering stole. He was solid ebony, thick through the waist.

"What's going on down there?" my father yelled.

"Teamwork," I yelled back.

The television turned louder.

I held Zulu at arms length. Then I sniffed him. He smelled like Africa. He smelled like savannas and swelter and stacks of polished bone. His skirt had jagged fronds. He wore a necklace of teeth and gripped a spear, notched and ready.

Finding him was like every Christmas, all of them, at once.

Until I noticed a card, tied to his calf.

Oh darling, it said, in a scratchy mannish quill that was not my father's. *Oh, my love...*

I closed my eyes, feeling sick.

...I need you. Now more than ever.

There were proclamations and entreaties. "*...room for you here... we can live...*"

There were XXXs and OOOs. There was a foreign stamp.

Always, it was signed, at the bottom, *always, Carl.*

I dropped Zulu, wiping my hands on my pants. I grabbed the broom, angrily chuffing dust, which rose in tiny clouds. I made long pointless swipes, twelve, fourteen, sixteen. Twenty-four, twenty-eight, thirty. The broom made an ugly sound, swish (Carl), swish (Carl), swish. I counted to a hundred, and then two. And then three. My hands were red and raw, splinters and bits of paint digging in. Six hundred. Then seven.

At nine-o-nine, I gave up.

Why did it matter where he came from? I found him, and he was mine.

I grabbed Zulu and apologized, hugging him close. I tore the card off his leg and sailed it into the corner, where it disappeared among the clothes and books and everything else my mother had left behind.

"What the hell is that?" My father said, watching a commercial. A Chicano family couldn't believe how fresh their laundry smelled. Then a nurse discovered a better napkin.

"It's nothing. I found it."

"Get rid of it," he said, "not in my house."

"His name is Zulu," I explained, "he's good luck."

"No such thing," my father said, and then tried to swipe Zulu out of my hand, almost falling over. I steadied him. He turned the television louder, rubbing his knee.

"You heard me," he finally said.

"I heard you." I agreed.

I locked the door. I put Zulu on my dresser, where I could watch him from the bed, and then got under the covers. It was warm and musty, but somehow different. Even the light had changed. I closed my eyes and imagined Zulu hunting, pointing his spear, directing skirmishers and brush-beaters. I imagined him building huts made of woven grass and rhino dung. I imagined him defeating rivals and hyenas alike (tug). I imagined him dancing and drumming, the eating of Zebra steaks and pleasuring of multiple wives (tug, tug).

My father knocked on the door.

"Son?"

"Not now."

"Buddy?'

"Go away."

If I had a radio, I would have turned it loud. If I had a helicopter, I would have flown south.

"Listen, now, really."

"Who's Carl?" I asked.

The knocking stopped. The hallway boards creaked. He shifted weight, right to left.

"Always, always," I said.

The television volume went up, fake laughs like the bowing of a thousand cricket legs. The window was gray and my blanket was gray and Zulu's agate eyes shone.

The next morning, I dressed early and took the bus downtown, classifieds open, likely positions circled in red. The driver was enormously fat and wore a beret. His name was Todd.

"Any luck?" Todd asked, every day.

"Luck is for losers," I answered, every day.

Then we'd both laugh.

Down the aisle, the other riders would try to catch my eye. They wanted to laugh too, share a little camaraderie, shoulder to shoulder for the long diesel slog. The thing is, we weren't all in it together. I was me, gripping the paper, making fake notations in the margins. They were them, hair and ears and feet, work and fart and banana. I found a seat alone and let them find their own jokes.

My first interview was on the 26th floor of a building that overlooked the river, new and solid and free of graffiti.

"Sign in," said the security guard, whose nametag said Tayshaun Clements. I wrote MIKE REED in careful block letters. Four in front, four in back. There was an undeniable symmetry. My father's name was Mike Reed and his father's name was Mike Reed. We were unburdened by extra syllables. It was better than a trust fund.

The thing is, we weren't all in it together. I was me, gripping the paper, making fake notations in the margins. They were them, hair and ears and feet, work and fart and banana.

"Fill in your purpose." Tayshaun said, pointing to the box I'd left empty. His head was bald, slick, and shiny. Paunch lurked beneath his uniform. A line began to form behind us.

"Purpose?"

"Your purpose? For being here? In the building?"

I bit the pen.

"Don't bite the pen," Tayshaun said.

I started to write *None*, but didn't. Then I wrote *Indeterminate*, before scratching it out. I finally settled on *Potentially employable*.

"Good luck." Tayhaun grunted, taking the pen and handing it to the person behind me.

"Luck is for losers," I told him.

"Mike Reed?"

I walked into an office that was barely furnished. Boxes were stacked in the corner. A pale man gave me the Limp Shake. "Marty Dill," he said, one letter away from symmetry. I felt bad for him. "Sorry for the mess. We just moved in."

A banner printed on computer paper hung on the wall. It read OFFSHORE MAGNET AND STICKER.

"So, Mike, tell me about magnets," Marty Dill invited, crossing his legs. His fingers met over his chest, like a church roof. The wall behind him was freshly painted, gleaming white. His forehead, without hair, faded into nothingness. Nine minutes later he stood without offering a hand.

"We'll make a decision by next week."

In the hall a woman turned sideways to let me pass. She had a resume, a matching skirt and sweater, her hair straight back in a barrette.

"Run." I whispered.

"Excuse me?"

She smiled, bright and open and actually ready to consider.

"Run." I said again, before she spun to meet Marty Dill and his limp fish.

"You still here?" he asked, leading her into the office.

It took forever for the yellow light to get all the way up to 26. I stood in front of the elevator with a group of men and women who'd just come out of a conference room. The name on the door said Amalgamated Bran. They talked and yawned with their bags and briefcases, confident in their tweed and double-breast. I assigned the number seventy-three to how much I hated them. When the car came, everyone got on, but I couldn't move. They held the door, waiting. I stuck out one leg, like a dowser.

"Are you coming?" said a woman with a mole on her cheek. *"Hell-lo?"*

They stared.

I stared.

The door closed.

It took two more tries to get to the lobby. Tayshaun was at his desk, pretending to read a book. It was called *DISASTER!*, the letters of the title in flames.

My brother lived with his girlfriend in an apartment downtown.

"You look pale," he said, on the couch in his boxers.

"The tanning salon was closed."

He stared at me.

My brother never thought anything was funny unless he said it. He was unemployed, too, but his girlfriend was a bartender who made a lot of money, cash.

"Any leads?" I asked.

He shrugged and opened a beer, a brand that claimed to be really cold.

"Not really."

He took a long swallow and then grimaced. "Living in this dump is practically a full-time job anyway."

The walls were decorated with posters for bands I'd never heard of. On the shelf was a ceramic dragon that you could inhale marijuana smoke from.

"How's the old fart?" he asked. They no longer spoke.

"Fine." I said. He nodded, exactly the same way he would have if I'd said Comatose or Flowering or Halved.

The Bartender opened the door with a bang.

"Oh, boy," said my brother.

"What are you doing here?" The Bartender asked. Her legs were wide, arms crossed, a stance that said Lesbian Volleyball Coach. It said you're this close to a shorts inspection.

"I'm thinking about moving to Cali," my brother whispered, staring at the ceiling.

"You're not going anywhere, slug," The Bartender told him, ushering me out, "but *he* is."

"I'm thinking about moving to Cali," I told the girl at RODS AND CONES. It used to be a chain but went under. You could still see the old logo, purple and orange, under the new paint.

"Good for you," she said, handing me a vanilla scoop. Her hands were sour, the fragrance of metal and old dairy. Her hair was in a short

"How could they not hire you?"

I shrugged. There were so many reasons. There was endless nuance.

bob. Her skin was completely white, possibly from being refrigerated all day.

"What's your favorite flavor?" I asked. She looked into my eyes, searching for sarcasm. It wasn't there. She shook her head and went back to reading the newspaper.

"Hired yet?" My father asked, standing in the doorway. I stood on the front step, cold.

"No."

He blew his whistle, tweet. He did it three more times. I stuck my fingers in my ears. I was wearing a tan sweater and tan pants.

"Are you going to let me in?"

"How could they not hire you?"

I shrugged. There were so many reasons. There was endless nuance.

He looked down at his crotch and shook his head. "What with all the LaTroys and DeWaynes in the world?"

"Are you going to let me in?" I asked again. I could see my breath, frosty and gray.

"Password." He said.

I sighed. There was no fighting it.

"Mike Reed. Solid. Balance."

He stepped aside and then went and sat in his chair, blowing the whistle in sad little tweets. I got a brush and stood behind him, running it through his thin hair, which refused to lie down. There was a commercial on television. A woman was concerned with her personal freshness. Then a basketball player challenged a life-sized soda to a game of one on one.

I went to my room and lay under the comforter with all my clothes on, looking at Zulu. It was seven thirty. Models hung from the ceiling on fishing wire. Flying Fortresses and Messerschmidts. Zeros and Migs. All of them were half-destroyed, missing pieces, wings, and props. I had been banging into them with my head since the summer I turned sixteen.

Barrelhouse

Zulu stood on the dresser, watching me.

Well? he seemed to ask.

I turned over.

Outside my window was the dead oak, a canopy of spindled black. My father had planted it the day we'd moved in. I imagined it coming to life. I imagined the sun pouring through fleshy leaves, sap pulsing from the center of the earth. Suddenly birds circled and dove, chirping their happy language (tug). Dogs frolicked, barking in volleys (tug). My mother's station wagon was back, parked in the driveway (tug, tug), the smell of bacon wafting up from the kitchen. It was all so suddenly and completely obvious.

"His name is Zulu." I told the girl at the ice cream store. She looked up at him, on the counter, glowering at a vat of Maple Almond.

"He's scary." She said. "Freaky."

"He's a warrior. He's good luck."

She dropped her paper on the floor and stood. She ran her finger along his base. It made me shiver.

"Where did you get him?"

"Carl." I said, by mistake.

"Who's Carl?"

"I found him," I said. "I think he was meant for me."

She nodded, then bit her lip.

"What's wrong?"

"Customers," she sighed, nodding toward a family peering in the window. The door opened, and a chime played a song for tired clowns. The children yelped and pushed and shrieked and tugged, grappling with each other's fat to see who would order first.

"What's good today?" Dad asked, happy and rhomboid. Mom chuckled, getting her purse ready. Then they saw Zulu sitting on the counter.

"Umm…" said dad.

"Do something," said mom.

One of the boys began to cry, and then the others joined in. Mom

"What's good today?" Dad asked, happy and rhomboid. Mom chuckled, getting her purse ready. Then they saw Zulu sitting on the counter.

herded them through the door while dad and his combover tried out a scowl. Their van made a tiny squeal as it left the parking lot.

"He is good luck," she laughed. "Can we keep him here always?"

"Not always," I said.

"My name's Danielle," she smiled, wiping down the blender.

"Is it a bong?" my brother asked.

"His name is Zulu." I said. "He's lucky."

"I saw that movie. With Michael Caine?"

"What movie?"

"*The Zulus.* They kill all the English with spears. And then eat them."

"No one would eat Michael Caine." I said. "All gristle."

He didn't laugh.

"I wonder where it came from?" He said, running his finger along Zulu's base.

"Don't." I said. "Touch."

There was a banging in the hallway. The Bartender kicked open the door, loaded down with bags of groceries.

"Can I get a little help?" she asked my brother.

"You better split," he told me, not getting up. The Bartender dropped one of the bags, vegetables and fruit rolling. She gave me a look like it was my fault. "Are you still here?"

I held Zulu at arm's length, moving toward her. She dropped the other bags, oranges thumping tile. There was fear in her eyes. My brother was still on the couch. He opened another *extremely cold* beer.

"Mark? Are you going to do something?" The Bartender whined.

"Mark Reed," he said, taking another gulp, "Solid. Balance."

I retrieved an onion from under the couch and took a bite like it was the world's tastiest granny smith. I gave her a big smile, all teeth. The Bartender moaned, stepping aside, as Zulu and I walked out the door.

Tayshaun had his feet up. I put Zulu on his desk with a slam.

"Holy shit," he said, spilling coffee, which smelled like rum. He walked in circles, scratching his neck, taking stock.

"I remember you," he finally said, looking at me, "Potentially unemployable."

"This is Zulu." I told him. "He's good luck."

"I dunno about luck, but he's a badass, I'll give you that."

Tayshaun refilled his cup. He pulled a flask from his boot and topped the coffee off, giving me a wink. I winked back. It felt so good, I did it again.

"You got a twitch?"

"No."

The lobby was empty. There was a new book on his chair called *SLAUGHTER!* The letters of the title dripped blood.

"So how much you want for Mr. Badass?"

"Zulu." I told him. "Not for sale."

"Everything's for sale," he said, emptying his cup.

"Not everything."

Tayshaun nodded. "Maybe you're quicker than I gave you credit."

"Maybe." I agreed.

"Siddown, Unemployable," he told me, kicking a chair in my direction.

"Thanks."

Tayshaun loosened his belt and then poured us a pair of coffees. After the second one, I told him about Carl. He nodded, listening. When I was done, he took a deep breath and said, "There as many Carls in the world as there is back doors."

We sat and thought about that for a while. Then he said, "Your Daddy didn't keep his locked, that's on him. Least you got a Badass out of the deal."

I nodded. He was so completely right.

Tayshaun reached over and touched the tip of Zulu's spear.

"Ouch!" he said, sucking his finger.

"Careful," I told him, and then winked. Later he let me help him water the plants in the lobby, all of which were plastic.

"Hey, buddy? Yeah, you with the doll."

A man caught up to me on the sidewalk. He wore a purple shirt, and his hair was slicked back. "A little old for dolls, huh?"

"His name in Zulu," I said.

"Sure, sure, I saw that movie. Mike Caine, right?"

I nodded.

"Lousy film," he said. "They blew the whole budget on sideburns."

He seemed to be having trouble swallowing. He shifted his weight, put his hands in his pockets, took them out and inspected his fingernails, which were heavily chewed.

"Anyways, I own Vincent's Photo Shop."

He pointed with his thumb. Behind us was a store with a sign that said *Vincent's Photo Shoppe.*

"My regular guy just quit. Walked out without a word. I seen you hanging around, I thought, I bet that guy needs a job. You need a job?"

"I don't know about cameras," I said.

He laughed. "Hell, neither do I. What you do, you take the rolls, fill out a form. Then we send it to the lab."

"That's it?"

"*Would you like a receipt, ma'am?*" he said, in a stage voice. "*Can I interest you in double prints, sir?*"

"I like pictures." I told him.

"Sure you do. You want the job or no?"

"Yes." I said, envisioning my father's face, hair and smile at attention. "But I don't work without my partner."

He frowned. "*Partner?*"

He held up his hands and took a step back. "You mean like your *boyfriend?*"

I showed him Zulu.

Vincent laughed. He held his stomach and made a big show of being relieved. He shook his head and shuffled his feet and wiped his eyes. He pursed his lips and snapped his fingers and stood on his toes.

"The doll? Sure, bring the doll. Hell, bring Tonto if you want. Just be here at nine."

"Deal," I said.

He touched his finger to his nose, and then walked back to the store.

I sat by the river with Zulu on my lap. Small boats went by, people fishing, standing on their decks drinking beer, once in a while a rusty barge. Danielle walked through the grass, shading her eyes, and then came and sat next to me, a small bag of take-out vanilla in her hand.

"I thought you were going to Cali."

"Maybe not." I told her. "After all."

"How's your friend?"

I picked Zulu up and looked at him. "He's a warrior."

She moved closer. I could feel her haunch against mine. "I forgot to ask your name."

"Tayshaun," I said.

She nodded and then opened the ice cream and fed me small scoops. I fed her larger ones. She poked the empty container onto Zulu's spear so that it wouldn't blow away. Somehow I didn't mind.

"I got hired," I told her, just when she said, "I got fired."

Then we both said, *"Really?"*

"The family complained. My boss calls me in the office and actually goes 'Devil Dolls and Chocolate Chip are *incompatible*.' "

She laughed, a delicate little peal that nearly crushed me.

"I'm sorry."

She waved her hand. "It's the best thing that could have happened. Or maybe *second* best."

I blushed. There was a good chance she was talking about me.

The sun was full and fat and warm. Couples strolled by. Children held balloons and dogs tore around in circles, their tongues pink and black. "I can't remember the last time I sat in the grass," I said.

"I know. For once I can smell something besides pistachio."

I took her hand and squeezed. She squeezed back. Below, water eddied through the sluice gates, which were huge metal slats that kept the river from rising up and drowning us all.

Featured Poet:

nancy slavin

Storm Watch from the Oregon Coast

I want to write about living on the edge.
But the wind blusters outside and the too-tall rose hedge

Slaps against the paint-peeled house. The sparrows are blown
Off their swinging ceramic feeder, flown

Not by their own direction but by rains
Which shoot down aslant and stain

The trunks of trees, soaked through to their north-faced moss.
Of course, I could write of loss,

The breaker-washed flotsam along the beach
And the refuse of jetsam flung from ships at sea,

But what use are remainders that remind us of
The sorrow of our fragility and our desperate need for love?

So here, a mile inland from the coast,
Storms strike against the headlands. A boast

Of power, omnipotence, and clout
While, hidden away, the rest of us wait the storms out.

A rose petal sticks against the pane, a bird tucks
Its bill under its wing, and I wonder: is it luck

That allows me to live so near the edge
Where my heart aches in joy for the very privilege

To know again and again with each wild, salty gust
I am not in charge nor do I ever want such lust?

Migration

The refuge is perfectly silent. Calm
east winds design the watery surface.
Eelgrass bows underneath. No need for alarm;
dawn breaks through the upland forest.

But then, a thrum of sound, a throng of squawks
approaches in reports so loud it hurts.
The sky goes black with arriving flocks
splashing down into the wetlands like gunshot.

For days, the babbling horde drops its yields,
scattering turns of phrase and scans of webbed footprints
overlapped in mudflats and trampled down fields
where any onlooker sees nothing but the chaotic.

Until one afternoon, when, versed by the season,
a million wings span west and set out past the estuary.
Leaving behind a little piece of rhyme and reason,
as one chevron, they fly as far as light will carry.

Anything I do, I always try to fuck with the form. Always, always try to fuck with the form. Why play something that's already been played? It doesn't make any sense to me. And even beyond that, even genre—why even engage in a genre? It just seems so limiting to me.

—Ian MacKaye

Ian MacKaye

Ian MacKaye has been one of the most respected figures in American underground music for twenty-five years. Whether as a musician in influential bands like Minor Threat and Fugazi or as co-owner (with former Minor Threat bandmate Jeff Nelson) of the intensely independent Dischord record label (www.dischord.com), MacKaye has established himself as someone committed to the concepts of individuality and integrity, putting them well ahead of profit and popularity. Unlike hoards of famous musicians who give lip service to pet social issues while raking in cash from their latest million-seller, MacKaye has consistently put his time and money where his mouth is, playing countless benefits for causes he supports and refusing to charge more than five dollars for performances.

Five dollars. That isn't a typo.

As an artist, MacKaye has made a career of defying musical expectations. When his seminal hardcore outfit Minor Threat broke up in the early eighties, he took up the guitar and formed the melodic, at times experimental Fugazi, a band whose reputation far exceeded the small venues the group played, their sound carrying through even to the most mainstream rock acts. With Fugazi on an extended hiatus, MacKaye has changed direction again, stripping his sound down to only a guitar and drums in his latest endeavor, The Evens, a duo that pairs him with ex-Warmers drummer Amy Farina.

In talking with Barrelhouse, MacKaye spoke about topics ranging from his earliest musical influences to what the word "punk" means to him after making music for two and half decades. The conversation began with MacKaye talking about the types of books he likes.

Ian MacKaye: I like fiction where people commit to a story. I think there's a tendency, especially for young writers, to take advantage of style to avoid having to commit to a narrative. I'm more interested in people who have a story. It doesn't have to be neat. It doesn't have to be tidy. It doesn't have to have an ending, you know? I think some of my favorite writing, once I got my head around it, [comes from people] like Raymond Carver, who just leave things. Somebody like Carver, I feel like there's an entire novel there and he just went in with a razorblade and snipped out an hour of it, and you have to figure out what happened before and what happened later. That's like life. That style is something I've seen emulated [by other writers], and there's no larger story. They just feel like it looks writerly.

Barrelhouse: A lot of young writers tend to emulate a style they like before finding one of their own.

IM: In music there's a parallel to this, with a slight adjustment. In terms of my interest in music, what I find endlessly fascinating is people's struggle with their instruments as they learn them. They pick up their instruments, they're engaging with music, they're inspired by something, and they want to sound like that thing. So they play what they think is an emulation of that music. However, their relationship with their instruments is so completely different than the people who inspired them and it really sounds nothing like it, or very little like what they think it sounds like, and in that you have innovation.

Artist, in my opinion, means translator. An artist is somebody who, if they're, say, a visual artist, see things and then try to translate them to share them with people. If they're writers they hear or think things and they translate them for people. They kind of draw a circle around what they're thinking. They distill it in a way that people can get it. With a musician, of course, I think people hear things and they try to translate that. They try to recreate what they're hearing.

BH: Can you talk a bit about your earliest musical influences, the stuff you listened to growing up? Did your parents' taste have an effect on you? And how did that music influence the type of music you've made over the course of your career?

IM: In the very beginning, obviously, I listened to my parents' records. The first record I really recall hearing was a recording called "The Last Date" by Floyd Cramer. It was a great song, and my mother said I loved it. I played it over and over again. [My parents] had a Grundig, kind of cabinet style stereo/turntable, and I remember playing it, putting my head on the floor, and listening to it over and over until I fell asleep. The neighborhood I grew up in was largely families, but there was beginning to be hippie group houses and college group houses.

BH: This was in the mid-sixties?

IM: Yeah, mid to late. I was born in '62. So I think that my parents had hip friends, so I would hear the Beatles a lot, which I liked. And, you know, I heard Jimi Hendrix and Janis Joplin. Those are people that I really adored and still adore. All of those bands, I still love all of them. Then I remember meeting these kind of hippie kids in the neighborhood. I became friends with them. I was probably eight or nine years old and they were probably eighteen or nineteen. I started going through their record collections. There was a woman who had probably one crate of records and I remember just staring at that crate thinking, "Someday I hope I have this many records." She had, like, James Gang's *Thirds*. Jefferson Airplane's *Volunteers*. Herb Alpert and the Tijuana Brass. Just all of this, I think, fairly iconic, sixties major label stuff. But I was so interested—I was just tantalized by it. And of course the Archies had the television cartoon. The Monkees, obviously. The Beatles had a cartoon. Anything like that I would watch.

My parents were not really musicians. My mother played piano, but she was a sight reader—she could only play if she was reading. She loved music, and actually there's a family theory that part of the reason music became such a big part of my life was that when I was born, she had spent a lot of time playing piano when she was pregnant with me. Take it for what it's worth. The fact is, however, I started playing piano when I was three. I still play piano. I kind of consider it my basic/main instrument, but I can't read. Even though I've written a million songs on it, I forget them all. I can just sit down and make something. But it's my primary instrument in a way that I would probably never play it live. It's just my private thing.

So I think I just ended up listening to a lot of music. Anything I could get my hands on, really. And somewhere around 1972, I, of course, was really aware of rock. I knew about what was going on. And also my parents, you know, we were liberals. We went to St. Stephen's Incarnation, an Episcopal Church at the corner of 16th and Newton Street. It was a very radical, left church. What I mean by that is that it was fully engaged with the Civil Rights Movement, fully engaged with the anti-war movement, fully engaged with women's rights, fully engaged with gay rights. Stokely Carmichael spoke there. We had rock bands playing in the church. There was a sanctuary for protesters.

When Martin Luther King, Jr., was assassinated in April of 1968, it was just before Palm Sunday, and 14th Street was on fire. There was rioting and 14th was in serious chaos. Then, on Palm Sunday, the church left the building. The congregation marched down Newton Street and made a right on 14th. We marched right down the middle of all the mess and had a service in front of an abandoned building in the midst of these fire engines. The one thing I remember from that day, and this is significant I think, was this woman, Mother Scott, playing guitar. She was a country/blues singer and she was a member of St. Stephen's congregation. She'd put out a couple of records; she was great. But she sat on this porch and played some songs. And that music just seemed so powerful to me in that context. Music is always powerful to me. I'm just trying to give you a sense: I remember all of the music from that day. I remember hardly anything *but* the music.

BH: When did punk come into it?

IM: I guess I haven't quite gotten there yet. I was first totally intoxicated with Woodstock. I loved Woodstock. That movie just blew my mind. I think I saw it sixteen times in the theater. I owned three or four copies of the record. I was just fascinated by it. When my family would go on trips, I would look out the window looking for my concert. I really loved this idea of outdoor shows. And I loved smashing the guitars and all that. So I decided that I really wanted to be in a band. But I didn't want to play keyboards; I wanted to play guitar. My mom bought me a guitar from a garage sale when I was probably ten or eleven. It was totally screwed up, not playable really. She hired a neighborhood bully to teach me how to play it. This had a twofold reason. (She was a very smart woman.) Part of it was so I could learn how to play, but she also figured if she paid him, he'd stop picking on me. She was right.

But he didn't really know how to play guitar, either. She gave him ten bucks and he taught me how to play "Smoke on the Water" on one string. I could not understand how to make a chord on a guitar. At some point, I just realized that this is like the province of the elite. Music belonged only to Peter Frampton and Jimmy Page. They were like bluebloods. Obviously, I was never going to do it. There was a brief spell of time when we would go shoplift toy guitars just to practice smashing them, but the reality was I was never going to be in a band. Around that time, the mid to late seventies, I started skateboarding. I skated a lot. I had a skate team called Team Sahara. But we were totally a gang, basically. We were not sponsored. We got our own little jerseys. The members of that were Henry Rollins, Mark Sullivan—all these people who later on would be punk rockers. I don't know if you're familiar with the *Dogtown* movie, but it was sort of our version of that era.

At that point, Henry and I were listening to Ted Nugent. *Double Live Gonzo!* was like the Holy Grail for us. We loved that record. I was actually intrigued by [Nugent] because I didn't know much about his politics, certainly didn't have any idea about his right wing politics. What I did know was that he was straight—he didn't drink, he didn't take drugs—and I've always been straight. I was relieved to hear it about him. And also he was super visceral. When I saw him play live, it was incredible. He spit on stage. He cussed. This was unheard of. It was scary. And like many things that intimidate me, I go towards them. So he was really interesting. We just loved his music.

It was in probably 1977 or '78 that my friends in high school started getting involved with new wave. They were listening to The Ramones and Iggy Pop, maybe Devo. We started to argue about who rocked harder. I was just so adamant that Nugent kicked everyone's ass, and finally one of my friends lent me a stack of punk records. And it was The Sex Pistols' first record, The Jam's first record, Generation X, probably The Damned. That was probably October or November of '78. I took the records home and put them on. And at first it didn't sound like music to me. It was such a shock to my ear. The analogy I've used in the past to give people a sense of what I'm talking about is that if you grew up in America and you ate just hamburgers and French fries, hamburgers and French fries—that's dinner every night. Then you go to a Japanese or Chinese restaurant and they put dinner down in front of you, you just don't see it as dinner. And that's the way hearing that music was. I couldn't see it as music, but I knew it was music. I had to figure out *how* it was music. In listening to it, the filter peeled away, and it just opened my mind. I thought, "Wow, this is incredible music," and I became fascinated by it. Then I saw The Cramps in early '79 at Georgetown University. It was the first punk show I saw, and that gig was just mind blowing. I just thought, "Wow, here it is, this is the counterculture. This is the world I want to be part of. This is the zone where people are challenging conventional thinking. And that's what I want to be."

BH: All the bands you've been in have had their influences, but you're definitely trying to make something different with your music, too. Do you typically try to create a type of music that's never been made before, or is that more of an offshoot of the personalities involved in the bands?

IM: I think any time you enter into a creative process organically with other people, you're going to make something that's never existed before. It's only when you enter it deliberately or in a calculated fashion that you make referential music. I don't want to be referential. I don't have any problem tipping my hat to the music that inspired me. I've always said: Music kicked my ass; I only intend to return the favor. But what kicks my ass about music is the innovation, the freshness, that freedom. Anything I do, I always try to fuck with the form. Always, always try to fuck with the form. Why play something that's already been played? It doesn't make any sense to me. And even beyond that, even genre—why even engage in a genre? It just seems so limiting to me.

BH: All of your bands sort of defy characterization. Before Minor Threat, there was nothing like it. And Fugazi stands outside definition, too, although some people have tried to characterize it as emo. Even the The Evens is different. Some people have tried to call it folk, but it's certainly not that.

IM: I would call that desperate categorization. But better that than something else. At least it makes you scratch your head: "Folk, huh?" Whereas, if it was something like power pop, that seems so boring to me.

I want to engage with people. I want people to be engaged by music. I want to continue to challenge the idea of what music is. The limits that I think I exist under are my own limits, in terms of what I can actually do. My range in terms of singing and guitar playing, I can only do so much, but I feel like every band has the potential to be totally fresh if they just go for it. Just actually try. It's like when we started talking today, I mentioned this idea about people who commit to stories. Well I fucking commit to songs. I don't back away into a haze of genre. I certainly don't want to waste my breath singing about metaphorical, nonsensical things. There's a difference between people who do vocals and people who do songs. And a lot of times people approach things like, well these are the vocals, let's come up with some words. They don't really want to commit to any ideas; they just want to put a voice on this music. To me it becomes so dismissible, because a lot of times I see music or read things, and it becomes so evident that the creators don't care. And if the creators don't care, why should I? It's like, we're just passing time.

I've often said, in 1979 I turned the radio off forever. And that's the truth. I don't listen to commercial music. I just don't. Like yesterday, I was at a party and this song came on and everyone kind of lit up, and I was like, "What is it?" And somebody said, "Come on. It's Beyoncé." I said I know the name, but I don't know the music. I'm not trying to be an elitist; I just don't know it because I turned that radio off. And people ask, "Don't you feel like you're missing something?" The answer is no. In the time that you and I will sit here today, the total quantity of music that is generated—if you took all that music and stacked it up—would be more than we could listen to in a lifetime. There's so much music in the world—so why spend time listening to music that is so obviously being engineered to be manipulative, commercially minded, and ultimately just trying to get you to buy it? I want to hear music that comes from people who don't have a choice in the matter. I understand that advertising works. That's clearly evident, and we understand that on every front. Advertising works. We know. But I want to hear music from people who don't have a choice in the matter. I want to read books by people who don't have a choice in the matter. I want to see pictures from people who don't have a choice in the matter.

BH: How do you go about writing songs? Do you have a process?

IM: If I knew it, my life would be a lot easier. For the last year I've been essentially in a writing block. Since my mom died. I don't know how it works. I'm not nervous about it. I don't worry about it. It's just reality. Music will come. There's a certain kind of alignment involved for me. Things in my life have to line up. There has to be a certain amount of space, than you just hit the tap and things start coming out of you. And I think that the experience of my mom's death was so profound—I don't mean to say it was horrible. It wasn't horrible. It was actually almost incredible, but it was so significant. I think it, pretty much, you know, knocked my socks off a little bit. It's going to take me a while to kind of like...I don't think it's grieving, although that's certainly an element of it. Grieving manifests itself in many different ways. But I don't think it's, "Oh, he's grieving so he can't write." I don't think in terms like that. What I do think is that when a person has an opportunity to witness the world change—and this can be in the form of attending either the entrance or an exit of a life—it's a shock. It's a really tremendous experience. And I figure that it'll reverberate through me. My nature has always been to let those reverberations pass through, and when they finally do, I will be a better person. I'm always working to be better.

So, to answer your question: I have no idea how to write a song. Except to mean it.

BH: I want to talk a little bit about the idea of punk. It seems like such an appropriated word by a lot of people. Corporations take it. Even people selling stuff like soda take it. What does punk mean to you?

IM: First of all, I would say that all words are appropriated by corporations. Certainly the word "literature" is. The words "book" and "journal," too. It's just the nature of it. If people can make money, they'll try to make money. I mean punk for me, and obviously if you asked me this question twenty-five or twenty-six years ago, I probably would have had a different answer, because my context would've been different. But, talking about it now, it seems clear to me that punk is the free space. It's where new ideas can be presented. And it may not even be called punk—that's how free it is. That's what I call it.

I think that throughout history there's been mainstream society and then underground society. It's always existed, and it always will exist. In this particular era, that part of that society, the underground area, that counterculture society, is punk rock. That's what I consider punk. If someone says, "Well, I'm not a punk," they can still *engage* in the idea of creating music for music's sake, of writing for writing's sake—things that are divorced from pure and simple profit. To me that's mainstream society: the idea that everything has a price, this whole fallacy of what the market will bear, all this kind of stuff. In my mind, punk is just the term I use to describe the free space, an area, where new ideas have the possibility of being presented.

Rock clubs and commercial music and so forth basically require clientele because it's a for-profit industry. Someone needs to be buying the records, someone needs to be buying the drinks at the clubs, someone needs to be paying for the tickets, and all this sort of thing to fund this operation. That clientele that the industry relies on are the same people a band might call an audience. The problem with new ideas is that they don't have audiences; they haven't been thought of yet. When you always have to have an audience, what happens is you start falling back into referential stuff. Like ska music—you give it a classification, which hopefully will draw people in; or you say, like, this person is from this band. Ian MacKaye of Fugazi. They use that as a selling point. But new ideas, what I really love about the idea of punk, is it's a community of people that are open. They say, "We will gather and here's a stage." And the people playing on it will say, "Here's a new idea." And from there, you never know what might happen. There's always a potential for it.

That's what I think punk is. But I understand that I don't claim sole ownership of that word. I don't really care what people think. People will say, "You can't say that!" Well, of course I can say that. I remember a period of time when there were some very serious, politically minded people in the mid '90s who told me I had no right to sing about women's issues. My response, of course, is, "Fuck you. I can sing about anything I want to sing about." That's punk. It's just crazy. I feel like we can do anything.

BH: In conclusion, we ask of all of our interviewees one important question: What is your favorite Patrick Swayze movie?

IM: I have no idea. What movies was he in?

BH: *The Outsiders.*

IM: I saw it. I thought the book was much better.

BH: It was.

IM: I was a huge S.E. Hinton fan. I really don't give a fuck about Patrick Swayze.

Please see barrelhousemag.com for an
unabridged version of this interview.

:: by Brian Ames ::

T.J. arrives home to find the pumphouse door smashed in. Not only the door but the jamb, too, a deconstruct of splinters. In a wasp nest of sharp pokers, the hardware gleam of brass and oil. The failed, fucked lock jutting out. There's a streak of bootblack next to the keyhole.

T.J. thinks, whuh? and stands before the crushed woodwork. He peers into the gloom inside, thumbs hooked in his carpenter's belt, and sees a torn network of webs crossing the suggestion of wooden handles and unmade forms: pumphouse guts, a scythe, hoes, rakes, axes, a dozen kinds of shovels. Shit under tarps. The concrete bunker of the wellhead—its cement discus cap. Spiders and their sacs. He looks through the door as if he surveys a desert prairie at twilight, waits for a crescent moon to rise above a massif horizon.

Now he is in a 1974 Plymouth Roadrunner raising a creosote cloud trail across hardpan. There is cloth sliding up damp skin, the urge of fire, the shape of her, penetration and movement above seat fabric that has held the day's violent heat. His vision sweeps through the dust of windows—saguaro, stinkweed, bur sage, Joshua tree—and he stands now again in front of the pumphouse like he's never left, never been anywhere but here, now, at this moment. He is pierced with ache, run through with one of the pumphouse implements.

This is Michael's work. His bipolar son, who repeatedly breaks into the house and steals, has now expanded his megalomanic range. The drugs are not working, or Michael's not taking them. One of the two. But the pumphouse, for Christ's sake. Why the pumphouse?

T.J. peers around the fractured door, seeking afterimage. He senses vacuum, but not, at first, its shape. Light is diffused herein, its migration across old panes occluded by untended grime. Motes of it barely bleed in—it suppurates, one might say, like a picked wound. Its wan presence reveals nothing, and T.J. has to invoke another sense. After a minute he resolves a protoform: rubber, chrome rims and spokes, handlebars. It is a bicycle, gone missing. His daughter's bicycle is the thing that's not here.

Of course. T.J. has recently forbidden Michael use of the family car. But the boy has places to go, people to see. Manic episodes to spew. Roaring empty raw desolations of depression to ford. He's going to get his fucking wheels one way or another. Thus the smashed-to-bits door and missing bike. Kendra, T.J.'s daughter, is going to be pissed.

True, she comes home from school, discovers the trashed shed and her missing locomotion. "Dad! Mike's ripped off my bike!"

"I know sweetie, I know. He'll be back with it." T.J. hopes. And in the same breath, hopes not. The little bastard. The shrinks said—no, they promised—the meds, the counseling, would work. Instead he's running around like a goddamned ape. The rural town has become Michael's jungle of waves. He crests, he troughs. The town watches and suffers. Seventeen, dosed, and potentate-of-the-world/pile-of-shit. Sheila, his wife, keeps saying, "Give it time, Teej, give him time." She would.

A (partial) list of Michael's thefts:

Money from his father's wallet, on numerous occasions. Money from his mother's purse, as often. His father's portable CD player he kept in the garage, because Michael is self-medicating and needs cash. His father's coin collection, also for the fence.

Other transgressions:

Truant from school, Michael was locked out of the house—he arrived home before T.J. and Sheila. So he busted out the window, climbed in dragging blood through the bathroom, up the hall. A trail of bipolar AB-negative streaks.

He steals, secretly, in these ways: When he makes love to Sheila, he closes his eyes and sees a desert. Sees the shape of her, feels the sweat of her skin, hears her come in the half-light of a high wilderness night.

Michael threw the tree over last Christmas, displeased with his present. Sheila's glass ornaments shattered like ice chips.

Michael threatened his sister with a broken beer bottle after smoking dope. She fled the room, begged the parents to send him away.

Michael played first-chair trombone in his high school's stage band. Held one single note for a solo during the bridge of a fast number. Smashed brass over his director's jazzy shoulders when the man complained. T.J. and Sheila sit in the school counselor's office. The man drips concern from a face like a well-meaning pug dog. "We need to work together on Michael's issues." Issues, as if they are chromosomal, genetic, congenital. Listed, categorized, as if a plan can be wrought and executed against them. The counselor doesn't know T.J. has long given up, or that Sheila—bravely countenanced—is not terribly far in tow. And what the counselor actually means, anyway, is we can really offer no solutions here. Michael is placed in a special school, lasts two months. Drops out to sail those waves.

That's when T.J. cut off the driving privileges.

"O.K.," said his son. "Well then, fuck you."

Also, T.J. steals secretly from his wife, from the reservoir of her fidelity. It is not so different. Layer his infidelity—if in thought only, not deed—over his son's bipolarity. Sins of the fathers visited on the sons, that sort of thing. His head and guts ache when he considers this. He steals, secretly, in these ways: When he makes love to Sheila, he closes his eyes and sees a desert. Sees the shape of her, feels the sweat of her skin, hears her come in the half-light of a high wilderness night. That Roadrunner's rocking. His ears ring with recall.

Who do you love? T.J. knows the answer to this question. He wants to call out her name when he grasps Sheila's fingers. He wants to shout as she opens under him, locks her knees around the force of his hammer. The tip of him soars like planets. He closes his eyes and thinks of the dope man's girlfriend. He unflexes like a slipped cord, stirs through her slick fluid, withdraws. Thief. Guilty.

For twenty-two years he's been smuggling secrets.

He crossed the summer desert from Nacogdoches, Texas, to Bakersfield, California, in thirty-one hours once, moving product. A hundred and five, a hundred and eight degrees most of the way, at eighty-five miles per hour. North through Dallas to Oklahoma City, then west on I-40 through Albuquerque, Flagstaff, crossing into the Golden State at Lake Havasu, further through Barstow. Traversing the flat like an air-breathing ramjet.

In the Roadrunner's trunk, a kilo and a half of dried Colombia, plastic tarp-wrapped but still sweating from its own moist narcosis. The girlfriend of Marquez, his dope man, lounged like an ocelot in the passenger's bucket seat. "She needs a ride out to California," Marquez had said. At the moment of commission, T.J. believed it was to watch over the grass, to ensure the transaction happened with no funky shit going down. Marquez explained he was too busy to go. The dope man held his hands up, palms cupped, shrugging: "There's a whole new crop of freshmen at Austin." That was enough explanation for T.J. That and the fact the dope man was willing to pay him solid dollar for the move. As for the girlfriend, T.J. didn't care—she was small, friendly, stunning. Her eyes—my God, T.J. remembers those brown eyes, that black hair, red merlot-pulp lips in his dreams, at the job site, in the shower, in bed when Sheila joyfully collects him.

The girlfriend was a roadhouse bartender outside Nacogdoches city limits, down on the road to the reservoir. T.J. never learned how she got mixed up with Marquez. She was Mexican, Spanish, maybe Brazilian, he assumed—she later corrected that assumption with the claim she was third-generation, her grandfather Nicaraguan.

They'd crossed the New Mexico state line, Bad Company and

Lynyrd Skynyrd pounding from oversized speakers, and stopped for beer and wine at a service station. Then they were finished pumping gas and popping bottle caps. He opened the door for her. She settled in the seat sienna-skinned, with calves like creamed cocoa. Her thighs sucked an already short skirt higher, and he flashed on white cotton. Took a good long look, which she saw. Slowly, with a smile aboard, she let him see, made him see, and then smoothed down the delicate fabric with fingers of promise. He bulled around the Roadrunner's rear deck pushing a horn. Glancing through the back window, T.J. caught the sweep of her eyes in the rearview mirror.

They made it thirty more miles, almost to Tucumcari. She flirted like a kite in gusts, slouched in the seat, the skirt riding up again. She wanted to know what "T.J." stood for, but he wouldn't give that up. The airstream roared through the open windows, and he had to shout at her to be heard. He could swear she kept looking at the gearshift, then at his midriff. She raised an eyebrow, licked her thick lips, shouted back.

"What?" he yelled.

"It's hot!"

It's hot! She shrugged, pulled her shirt up and off, flung it in the back seat. Her breasts pulled him off-road on a cattle trail. He drove through the rough to the base of a mesa, pawed at her. Back there, she nodded, at the rear seat. There he tasted her beery mouth and the honeyed sweat of her skin, her bright nipples. He breathed in the exotic pollens she gave off. He pulled that skirt up and that cotton down, parted that flower, sluiced through her like a blade, dropping dew everywhere, exploding like a small nova.

Her name was Marta. He never forgot her name; he never will forget. Marta... What alchemy she performed across the Southwest, through Arizona, across the Mojave. Turning him to gold, every part of him, under a blue sky that faded brilliant white at the horizon. Riding him across the heat, across twenty-two years, across the dopamine-producing pocket of his brain.

Doing the deal in Bakersfield, then gone.

Two reams of paper and a print cartridge later, Michael stares from a thousand telephone poles: HAVE YOU SEEN ME?

Can he honestly say, now, that he's weary of this old story? He daydreams constantly about finding her—even now, more than two decades later, denying his own culpability for the reason why that is not possible.

Sometimes he wishes it never happened. Really, with all his heart. He denies it, this high desert pre-AIDS, pre-political correct, mid-70s, high on marijuana and beer and red wine fandango. And what followed it, in Bakersfield.

T.J. lifts the framing hammer and strikes. Every time the hammer hits the nailhead, every time that slim nail drives pine studs, he blinks a new past into existence. He raises the hammer for another blow. He blinks away perspiration.

It's been three and a half weeks since T.J. discovered the smashed-up pumphouse. He and Sheila have reported Michael's disappearance to the cops, to his shrink, to the parents of Michael's known friends. To the school, in case Michael makes a contact there for some bizarre reason. They have plastered Tacoma and the University District and Fremont with flyers T.J. made on the computer. Two reams of paper and a print cartridge later, Michael stares from a thousand telephone poles: HAVE YOU SEEN ME?

But even in the midst of this, T.J. can think only of Marta. While a house goes up around him it's four weeks, five weeks, six weeks—a change of season—and Michael's flyers run with ink and the rust of their own staples. The bond sheets fail at the corners. They are rain-soaked, wind-dried. Michael's picture flutters, tears at corners, floats to asphalt. Passing cars throw him up to the sky again. He hovers and spins in their passing wakes, falls with leaves, clogs drainage grates.

Sheila is crying in the front seat. She and T.J. are driving through the U-District on a Saturday in light rain. Traffic is hosed because there's a Husky game, Brigham Young in town, fresh-faced Mormons everywhere coping with the un-Utah-like rain. New paper occludes what remains of Michael on the poles: The Wild Debbies are playing O'Hennessey's. Some sort of grunge-cum-'70s/psychedelic rockers, if the paisleys that decorate the flyer mean anything.

Sheila is dismayed that Michael's flyers are gone, or ruined. Her guts are cracked in half for her son, shredded like the seasoned paper. She suggests they layer more Michael flyers on poles.

T.J. wants to be through. "What the fuck for?" he snarls. God help him, he wants only to get back to her. Sheila recoils against the passenger door. His rage—spat like a sleek, steaming missile—ricochets inside the car. Fire, smoke and propulsion, it overroars the blower jetting through shark gills above the dashboard. T.J.'s muscles and tendons want to rise through his skin. His eyes are bugging, no lids.

"Jesus Christ, Sheila." He stares like Charlie Manson—all he's missing is the tattoo swastika. "He left, but you don't get that do you? He left—he didn't want us. He didn't fucking need us. The little shit-bag motherfucking cocksucker just up and left. Fuck him! Shit!"

T.J. looks up at brake lights.

There is a substantial bang of steel and glass. The airbag blows up in his face, a flour explosion. Sheila stars the windshield with the side of her head just above the right temple. Failed hoses shoot fluid everywhere. Neon-piss antifreeze flows a runlet into the gutter. Lookie-loos point. Some do-gooder tries Sheila's door, yanks it free with a metallic crack. Blood oozes down her cheek as she lolls stupidly. The do-gooder encounters her bleeding concussion and a pasty T.J., tears streaming down pancake-meal cheeks. Salt rivulets flay open nude flesh on the dusty face of this man.

The smell of an accident in rain hovers above the sidewalks.

T.J. is with Sheila in a shared hospital room. The other occupant has a concussion too—they're in the smashed-head ward. The bellows of pumps and sucking pressurized tubes sough across a cubicle the nurse pulled around them, fabric hanging from ceiling tracks. This is a privacy for the slightly maimed. Sheila's temple is bandaged. She trails nasal tubes, intravenous spikes. T.J. thinks in all of this she has taken on the appearance of an appliance, plugged in but cooking nothing.

It's funny, how she lays there in a gown, inert: She never sleeps on her back, yet this is the way she rests now. T.J. recalls Marta sprawling in the Roadrunner's back seat. This is different. The doctor keeps repeating Sheila should pull out in a couple of hours. This is not a coma, but a deep, deep sleep. But a couple of hours and more have passed. T.J. has kept this vigil for two days now.

As T.J. watches, he wonders about Sheila's dreams. There aren't any, he knows. He's been watching her lids. There is no REM flutter, not one instance. The nurse comes in to tell him visiting hours are almost up. Will he go home or fill out a special form to stay? He takes her clipboard—writes his name, address, phone, other coordinates, again, like last night, on the form. Then he stretches out in the chair and scans Sheila's bruised face. He pulls a blanket around him. He relives an urgent moment cycling deep in him, where he lifted Marta's legs and slipped the underpants up over her thighs and calves, pulled them in a cotton tangle from her feet. How can he conjure that image and its fundamental scents here, now, in the presence of his not comatose but deeply sleeping wife? Can he recall the first time Sheila let him see her there? The first time she made a gift to him of that? He smiles: Yes, he can. The memory is not as vivid as that of Marta, but is nevertheless there. He is relieved. His guilt, which he has—years now—so carefully managed, finds a sort of tentative mitigation.

He remembers Sheila from a job site. She is the daughter of the man who had ordered the house built, come around to stare at the structure going up and the men who were putting it there. They had completed framing and were moving to installing the trusses—tough, sweaty, fucked-up work. T.J. remembered it was a morning straight out of Indian Summer—some time mid-September when the sun piled in as insistently as it had on any day during August or July. Sheila had arrived with her father, stood under T.J. while he made truss connections.

"Excuse me, miss," T.J. had said, with politeness and managed reserve, from the rafters. "It would be great if you'd stand over there."

He pointed with his hammer across the plywood floor to a place near a framed load-bearing wall—it would form the division of dining room and kitchen. "I'd hate to drop anything on your pretty head."

Sheila pretended to not understand. She looked up at him, squinting out sunlight. "Then don't." She folded her arms under her breasts. Pushing them toward him, he thought. But she got it, smiled, backed away. She reached the retaining wall, watched him work.

She made repeat visits to the site, the pair more interested with each completed step in the home's raising. In October they arranged a date, to smoke grass and drink Annie Greensprings in the unfinished basement. It was a harvest evening—she harvested him and he her, on blankets spread over the hard concrete floor. He closed his eyes—the blankets became Roadrunner seat fabric, the walls and joists around him desert. That was in 1979. Did he love her then, at that moment? They married in 1980, had Michael a year later. Surely, by then he loved her. T.J. worked jobs all over the Seattle area, rose to foreman. He opened his own general contracting company, but mismanaged it into the hands of high bidders. Sheila held him aloft out of shit during this time—was it then that he loved her? Kendra arrived in 1989, just as Michael began exhibiting inexplicable behaviors. They were weird episodes of disconnect—he runs a pencil into a schoolmate's palm, swipes change from his second-grade teacher's desk. At home, he starts pounding ants with his daddy's hammer on the cement sidewalk that runs from the driveway to the front door. He unzips on the playground and tells a girl she ought to touch his penis. The school had attempted a progressive response, requesting a meeting with T.J. and Sheila in which recommendations were bravely whispered. Michael's pediatrician was more straightforward: He needed counseling, even at eight.

But counseling required money T.J. couldn't sustain on a hammerer's take. They took Michael to two appointments, made a pair of late rent payments. The counselor's idea had run into eight, maybe ten, sessions. Missing the third appointment, T.J. strained under the notion of failed fatherhood, stacked this atop his unrelenting fantasies and guilt. How would he have raised Marta's child? What would he have done differently? While Kendra grew up perfectly, Michael grew out spasmodically. The boy suffered sleep disorders, trouble eating, outrageous highs, crushing lows. He walked in his sleep, captured and broke animals, beat up neighbor kids after the bus stopped, laid in bed all day scarcely able to move. T.J. turned up the gain on work, twelve, then fourteen, then sixteen hours a day. Sheila dealt with Michael alone. When cash began to go missing, T.J. adapted the idea that force must be met with force. Michael denied the theft; T.J. threw him against a wall, held him there slightly off the floor. Spat invective in his son's face. Not here! Not under my roof!

T.J. flounders in half sleep, lacing these memories with those of Marta in the desert—he's in Michael's face, then between Marta's legs. He's at Michael's principal's office, then tasting Marta's slick skin. Michael's trombone slide bends itself around the director's shoulders, and there's the fine peachy down of Marta's upper thighs, New Mexico sun glinting off the energy of each hair and drawing him to the unforgettable locus of those legs. I'm sorry Marta, God as my witness, I'm sorry. The fabric he weaves in the chair at Sheila's hospital bedside is shot through with failures of his own, everything a pale shadow alongside the raunchy Nacogdoches-to-Bakersfield route. Could he go back and undo it, reverse the trip? Take Marta and the dope from California to Texas, unscrew her, un-fuck his mind?

"Marta," he mumbles.

"Teej?"

"Marta." He is floating above the desert floor, all erection and remorse at once.

"Who's Marta, Thomas? Who is she?"

Sheila is conscious, talking funny with the tube shoved up her nose. In fact she has been awake for more than an hour, cracking through a thrumming ice cloud, a hammering in her right temple like T.J. has visited framing blows upon her. She's heard him mutter the word Marta numerous times, as well as speak Michael's name. She remembers Michael is missing, for weeks now maybe, but that's all she remembers, and wonders what—no, who—is Marta.

"She's a woman I loved once." T.J. emits this stark admission from a state between sleep and waking.

"Once?"

"Still," he whispers.

T.J. and Marta arrived at Bakersfield with her fluids still drying on him. Thirty hours from Nacogdoches, no sleep, just the pot and beer and wine and sex, the last a pull-over on this side of Barstow. She fucked him on a jacket spread aside the Roadrunner, next to a gigantic irrigation pump. Neither of them entertained any notions this wasn't the last time. So they made it hot and long like a storm. They stank and held grit in the folds of their skin. His beard was coming in.

The Bakersfield pusher peered through blinds after T.J.'s second fusillade of knocks. The man's eyes wandered over Marta, out onto the street, casing the Roadrunner. Marquez, the Texas dope man, had said to look for the '74 Runner—the kilo and a half, plus Marta, would be inside. "And we'll be square?" Marquez had asked. "We see," the Bakersfield pusher said. "Depends if she real nice to me."

The pusher cracked his front door, released chains. He stood between the frame, jeans and motorcycle boots and a silk shirt that hung unrestrained by his belt. The man made a quick assessment of T.J., took another lingering draught of Marta. His veined eyes left trails on her. The pusher looked at T.J. again. "You got my shit?"

"I'm here from Marquez," T.J. said.

"Who this?" The pusher nodded at Marta.

"This's Marta, Marquez's lady."

The pusher appraised her more closely. "Marquez, he a lucky fucker."

"That's right," Marta said, stared him down.

The pusher laughed from his guts. "You can come on in," he said, waving them across the threshold. "Smoke a bowl with me, we talk about it."

T.J. and Marta entered the front room, filled mostly with a long couch, an end table, and a scratched-up coffee table with a waterpipe on it. There was a huge beanbag chair in a corner next to stereo speakers, a poster of Jim Morrison and the rest of The Doors pinned to the wall above the stereo components.

The pusher pulled up a single chair and sat opposite the coffee table from them. He fished a cellophane bag from his jeans pocket, retrieved some pot from inside, loaded the bong. The trio passed it around.

"I could use a shower," T.J. said.

The pusher ignored T.J.'s icebreaker, instead broaching the subject of business: "Marquez say you bring me one-point-five kilo."

"Yeah."

"Where the one-point-five?"

"Trunk of the Roadrunner. You want me to get it?"

"Shit no, fool. Not till it dark out, man." He looked over at Marta to share that he believed T.J. to be an unschooled, unsophisticated lightweight. Surely she must have noted this on the drive over. She refused eye contact.

"Marquez say she part of the deal, too."

Marta's eyes snapped from her skirt to T.J., then to the pusher. "I don't follow you," she said.

The pusher laughed. "He say you product, too, little girl." He held his hands up in the air as if to indicate none of it was his idea, that it had all come from Marquez. But that, nevertheless, a deal had been made. To modify it now, even with the authority he possessed as its prime beneficiary, seemed to him unbusinesslike. Seeing that neither of his guests understood, even now, where he was going with this, he elaborated: "Marquez tell me you the ginch come with the dope." He turned to T.J.: "He makin' somethin' right to me with this bitch."

T.J. just then understood. Marta had been sent with the dope as some sort of reparation, a peace offering between two dope men with a beef. Over what, he couldn't imagine—money, some score gone awry, cars, other women. "Marquez never said nothing about this to me."

"Call 'im up, man." The pusher reached at the end table for the phone.

"Look, man," Marta said, stopping him. "You ain't touching me."

"Fuck I ain't." Then the pusher took another nonchalant hit. He turned to T.J.: "Sit down here and help yo'self. I'm gonna go upstairs and fuck this whore—see whether Marquez and me's even."

Fear immersed Marta, then a broiling outrage. She pleaded with T.J. with those eyes, as if blood were flowing from them. Do something! He looked away from her. I have to think, I have to think, doesn't she understand I have to think?

"Look," T.J. started, stopped. He gathered himself again, cast a reassuring glance at Marta. "Look, that ain't goin' down here tonight," he said. The dealer exhaled smoke, placed the bong back on the coffee table.

"It ain't?"

"No."

The dealer pulled a pistol out of his belt and set the piece on the coffee table, snub nose pointing at T.J. The two men looked up and locked gazes. The pusher nodded at the weapon.

"You sure?"

T.J. was silenced. The dealer turned to Marta. "You sure?"

"Asshole," she said. The comment could have been directed at either the pusher or T.J., or, most likely, both.

"Yeah, and I be all over yours in a few minutes."

There was stillness in the room as densely packed as if all the desert and flatland T.J. had traversed with her, all the cacti and mesas and hoodoos and small dry-gulch towns they had passed for thirty-one hours, all the delicious sweaty sex and sucking and salt, were shoved rudely into its confines. T.J. forced his own breath to inhale and exhale, his own heart to bang. He sought to muster some manner of solution, some brave internal courage he had a feeling wasn't there—never had been there—but shriveled in the raw presence of the pistol. The power of the Bakersfield pusher seemed like omnipotence. T.J. slumped in the couch.

"You go on an' get that shower you was askin' about," the pusher told him. "You," he picked up the piece and trained it on Marta, "come with me."

She sat with her arms across her breasts, staring straight at him. Abandoned, she made a vow: "Never."

The pusher attempted a semi-precious pleading that was really, at the core of it, simply cruel: "Come on, baby. You so fine, you like it with me."

Marta lifted herself off the couch, stood grinning. She wrenched her skirt and panties down. She pulled the top over her neck and stood in a pool of clothing. She flung hanks of un-shampooed hair around behind her.

"See this?" She smiled like a hooker.

"Yeah, baby, I see."

Her smile snapped off. She tucked her lips, folded them up with hate. Her eyes fired shells of her own while his cock rose at his fly.

"Look at me, my eyes," she said. He tore away from her pussy, her flat stomach, her breasts, locked on, saw her rancor. "You will never, ever fucking touch this," she said. "Marquez touched it—I made him crazy for it." She giggled without smiling. "He touched it." She gestured at T.J. on the couch. "All the way from New Mexico to here." She watched the pusher glance T.J.'s way. "I made him into a child," she said. Her breasts lifted high and perfect, the nipples erect like bright rubies. A bead of mercury sweat rolled down the lovely cleavage between, rolled clear to her navel.

"But you..." She waved a single finger at him and barely whispered. "Never."

He shot her through the chest. Blew her back out in carmine spray and bits of bone and organs and flesh onto the dirty wall behind the couch. The blast threw her onto the sofa, next to a flinching T.J. She looked toward him, saw him trembling like a schoolboy, tears of fear beginning to form, saw he still refused to witness this.

"Look at me." She aspirated through strange, glottal fluids. "Look," she insisted, throat welling. T.J. turned slowly, met her indicting gaze. Then she died.

"Help me clean this up," the pusher said.

T.J. brought the dope into the house and helped the pusher wrap

Marta in the empty tarp. They threw her body into an arroyo out west of Bakersfield. Covered the tarp with busted-up wood and stones. T.J. remembered asking, "What about Marquez?"

"I take care of that fucker," the pusher said. "You just book."

And T.J. did, he booked, in the Roadrunner with Marquez's advance to San Francisco, then Portland, then Seattle. Every time he passed California Highway Patrol, or an Oregon state trooper, he was sure they knew and, mystified, they didn't give chase. He called his mother in east Texas and told her he was taking a break from school. He held odd jobs all the way north: the stuff of his own private diaspora. And then that surety—that he would be discovered—faded with months, and years, then Sheila and two decades. He never knew another thing about what happened in California, or Texas.

T.J. makes this confession to Sheila in their dining room, hovered over coffee and cigarettes. It is the second morning after she's out; the stitches above her temple look like an insect where her hair was shaved back. His wife draws this secret, two decades worth of smuggled product, from him. She is unwilling for his sake to let go of the name Marta. Who is she? What is she to you?

At first he says, Don't worry—she's long in the past. But that doesn't seem enough. Truth is, Sheila's heard this name before at odd moments. In their bedroom washed backward through the prism of his dreams, compressing color into black mottled light. She has felt the word before, not spoken, but emanating from his pores as he labors over her, inside her.

Above linoleum, on a Formica tabletop, he tells her the story. A Nacogdoches-to-Bakersfield high desert run. That's all it was supposed to be. Sheila doesn't interrupt and Kendra is still sleeping, so there's time for all of this to emerge. There it is, on the table, like an excised carcinogenic organ. It beats once there between them, a dull-red throbbing heart or kidney, and stops. The two of them stare at it. T.J. believes Sheila's silence means he is, in her sight, ghoulish. She thinks maybe she has to leave. Admits so to the top of T.J.'s head as he watches wisps of steam rise and curl over his coffee cup. He lights another cigarette; the ashtray is mounded with them. There is a long silence, which he breaks: "Don't give up on me, Sheila." It is all he can think of saying.

"You gave up on Michael." She states this as if there is some connection. And there is, he knows, now.

"I know. But I need you now."

"Michael needed you."

"I need you and Michael now. And Kendra."

T.J. feels indescribably dark. He needs his wife to shine a light in the dark places of him, this awful hole. "I'm sorry," he says, finally.

"You have to call someone."

"I know."

"In California, I mean. The police."

"Yes."

There's a wall-mounted telephone in the kitchen. The cord hangs like a helix, a beige kinked strand connecting a handset he soon will collect and ask for Information in California. It is the same phone that will ring in seven weeks, just before Christmas. Sheila will answer, accept the charges. It will be a collect call from Hartford, Connecticut. "Michael," T.J. will hear her say, hear her sobbing. "It's Michael, Teej." T.J. will take the phone. "Michael?" His voice will shake. "Come home, son. We've missed you so bad."

Today, though, the phone waits for him. California waits. Marta... He takes a drink of coffee, rises, lifts the handset. Hears that immutable tone...raises a resolved wrist. His fingers dance penitence. There will be lawyers, weeks, months of trial, maybe jail or prison—

In a California canyon, bleached bones in a nest of fluttering plastic call out in a newly configured morning:

You are forgiven.

karen schoenhals

The Sea Goddess and I

The Sea Goddess' billowing scarf...
—MARGUERITE YOURCENAR
Hadrian's Memoirs

I want something to happen to me
but nothing ever does. I draw the outline
of my hand, moving the pen around
my fingers.
My hands are plain and small.

In my fantasy, the sea goddess' billowing red scarf
billows back to me. I hold it
as we ride the sea. From time to time
she turns
to look at me. Her plans for the sea
rock in her head. I know them all.

Soon, we pass a village along the shore.
We know it's
just an invention. What is a village
anyway—lights, a certain number of houses,
people? Where does it begin
and end? The sea goddess does not hesitate
to ride right past the village.

When the wind wanes
and we rest, I hold the scarf
loosely. My hands
are plain and small. As the sea goddess turns
to look at me, the scarf
runs up through my hands.

Pilot

So many dials to watch, lights blinking like sleep
sailing past, like the things he meant to do. The plane's drone
is as calm as *Shh...* spoken by someone who never stops
touching him. Tonight, he is alone.

In daylight, he lands on the sky as if it were the ground
pounding it like a runner—his cheeks turn red.
When he's the most sad, he flies gently, upside down
dipping down, and the world fills his head.

Arrow in a Tree

For Barbara

The evening before you existed
young birds were talking outside
your mother's window. Her head was full
of misunderstood stories.
The birds talked late into the darkness.

After many years along the river
you and I found each other
as I looked up at some animal
moving from rock to rock
on the mountainside.

What you had heard was true—
sunlight was portioned out carelessly
near the river—it was abundant.
There you found feelings so intricate
no one had ever described them.
You knew they were your own.

Now, you are beautiful.
Any one precious thing you do
is visible and present,
like an arrow stuck in a tree—
not as an act of violence, but to mark a place
where love has been, and always will be.

Jasmine

In the daytime, in a neighbor's garden
the jasmine closes in upon itself
holding in its fragrance.
I arrange empty bowls on the dining table.

At night, suddenly
the jasmine blooms—fragrance bursts
from its white body and fills the air. From
room to room I wander, wanting
some touch—at least someone to lay her fingers
on the back of my neck. I turn the knob
to dim the lights, and fill the bowls, one by one
with jasmine—a kind of potpourri
at each place setting. I wait
for no one to come.

The Barrelhouse Invitational:
a Very Special Swayze Section

by Tim Hall

Swayze: A Poem

Tousled forelock stirs
Sultry breeze, bare
chest glistens
Summer eternal;
Swayze

"It's such a fine line between stupid and clever."

David St. Hubbins, *This is Spinal Tap*

We have a thing for Patrick Swayze. We admit it. We have a thing for Flannery O'Connor and Jonathan Lethem, too, but for some reason it is our love of Swayze, of flowing mullets and famous bouncers, tough as nails dancers and zen surfer bank robbers, that we chose as the subject for the second Barrelhouse Invitational.

We issued a challenge: using Swayze as your muse, create fiction, poetry, essays, comics, screenplays, quilts, paintings, doilies, whatever.

You took that challenge and you ran with it. The work that follows is, we are confident in saying, the finest Patrick Swayze-related fiction and poetry ever to grace the pages of any literary journal. Ever.

Sadly, we received no quilts or doilies, and we had to commission the painting on the opposite page on our own dime.

Needless to say, it was worth it.

So sit back, relax, and enjoy. And please, whatever you do, don't ever put Baby in a corner.

For information about upcoming Barrelhouse Invitational topics, visit our website at www.barrelhousemag.com.

Dirty Bird

Derrick S. Pyle

In the beginning there was nothing.

But after that, once we saw him dance—
His large hands slid up her back—
We knew him,
Magnificent specimen.

And then a ghost,
A bank robber,
A Queen:
Puddle jumpers
Trying to be jets.

None so believable as
The man who has strength and stun
In the humsugar of voice and step,

Until a pedophile.
Strength and humsugar drying,
Behold the aging maple.

You never see a man fade
Until you watch him die
Reborn as a sad, small creature.
Flint-headed sharpness
Strikes himself against former, convincing
Spark.

Pathetic
Ash-caked peddler
Emerging from a dungeon.
Former god to women
Smacks running young boy ass
And at this death of the old we believe again.
Donnie Darko couldn't recast the past,
So enjoy what lies
Beneath the turbine
And there he is...Patrick
Swayze.

by Dave Longaker

I Am The Cooler And You Are The Bouncers

I have always wanted to dance. I've never been able to, but I've always wanted to. I'm not talking about the waltz or tango or even The Pachanga—I'm talking about that cool combination of sock-hop grinding and mambo that only Patrick Swayze has mastered and seemingly injected into American culture.

But, to be honest, it's not just the dance that I've wanted—it's the entire Patrick Swayze persona. That tough yet tender, jaded yet hopeful, dumb yet smart, small yet big, I-am-the-cooler-and-you-are-the-bouncers flair that is equally unassailable by the rich, powerful, smart, strong, evil, supernatural, or even Communist. That's what I've wanted. You come from a redneck town that also boasts a private upscale college, and you realize that being Swayze pretty much sets you up to deal with all comers and be loved and admired by all. And who doesn't want that?

So a few years ago I went ahead and nicknamed myself "Little Buddy Jr." by telling my college friends they call me that back home, while telling my friends from home the converse. I told them all about how I've always wanted to dance.

And I danced. How I danced. A slow-dance contest was eventually won using several lifts I'd rehearsed while balancing on a fallen log. Brazenly sporting my signature skin-tight black muscle tee, black cinched-ankle pants, and Jerry Lee Lewis coif, the cut of my jib was right on time. Yes, our dance tunes were laughably anachronistic, and yes, I sang one of them, but the judges couldn't deny us. Or rather they couldn't deny Little Buddy Jr. Turns out, though, that winning a slow dance contest in this way is not such a great thing when you live in a redneck town.

This is when I realized that it may be wise to play down this facet of the Swayze persona unless you've half-mastered several forms of the martial arts, or at least until you understand some basic tenets of the more North American-centric defensive arts, such as hockey-fighting, bar-fighting, guerilla warfare, or desert combat. Or you have a switchblade embedded in your right boot. Or at the very least know how to take out a guy's knee. No matter how big your opponent, take out his knee, and he's out of commission. I just thank god that pain don't hurt, which made it much easier to stitch up my own wounds sans novocaine.

After the dancing thing didn't work out, I began dabbling in a wide variety of paid-by-the-hour-and-honest-because-of-it jobs. Bartender, bouncer, truck driver, mechanic, dance instructor. But I found myself constantly beset by king pins and fat cats as I unsolicitedly attempted to protect the underdogs around me. That really soured me on the bullies of the world, and my rage devoured me, and I killed. Shameful, I know, and I carry it with me like a Kentucky hillbilly holds a grudge.

Plus the money never really panned out. Oh, I had enough to re-place my shattered windshields and slashed tires on a daily basis and to treat my lady friends to the occasional cup of coffee (leaded, of course), but I found it hard to maintain the level of hairstyle that effectively ex-pressed the essence of my bad boy/pretty boy soul.

So, taking another page out of Little Buddy's book, it wasn't hard for me to make the transition to thief, charlatan, doctor in a devel-oping country, drag queen, and minor-league hockey player. Inevita-bly, these led me to the occupation of bank robber. Granted, I lost the hard-working-but-honest aspect along the way, but the pay was better and I wound up with a ton of time to surf, play tackle beach football, and study Zen Buddhism.

Which brings me to my real revelation: You'd be amazed at the parallels and synergy between Zen Buddhism, armed robbery, and Fear Factor-type action sports. When you have this epiphany, or shall I say when you've found the path to this enlightenment, you have truly become one with Swayze, the Bodhisattva of bodhisattvas and the William Burroughs of adrenaline junkies.

I'm there. And when you get here, you'll see how easy it becomes to move from a philosophical conversation to a kidnapping, or for that matter from sky diving to the Flamenco. You'll marvel at the simplicity of the complex and respect the wise yet uneducated elderly. Which, for the enlightened, is reward enough in itself. Why do you think we're always walking around with that dreamy, constipated look in our eyes, staring into what, to you, the unenlightened, must look like the distance or the ceiling? We are looking to our Inner Selves, grappling with the Pain of our Past, the Plight of Humanity, and the Injustice of the Poor. We're studying our inner mullet, its length, the way it sways in the wind and jerks to the side when we rear our lovely heads back like miniature ponies.

But that is not the only reward, because when you can count yourself among the enlightened, when you know when it's time to be nice and when it's time not to be nice—when, that is, you have found your Inner Swayze—you will, like me, Get the Girl. In the end, at least. You'll of course always have a soft spot for kids, and you'll be tough as nails when the law tries to take yours away. But your logic and judgment will be clouded by shame from your past and your search for the ultimate wave, and you will lose everything that's ever mattered to you and find yourself practicing headstands in the desert. And so shall you earn your karma.

But until that day, I am the cooler, and you remain the bouncers.

:: by Justin Taylor ::

FORT SMITH ★ ARKANSAS
A MONOLOGUE

"I'd be a rich man, it's true
If I could make a living out of lovin' you
These two hands know what to do
If I could make a living out of lovin' you
I'd be a millionaire in a week or two
Yeah, I could make a living out of lovin' you"
—BON JOVI

The radio plays one sloppy country cover after another. This station—if it is a station and not a tape—has no commercials. Or perhaps another option: the Citgo company runs this station commercial free...with one proviso. To wit—every three minutes or so the music is drowned out by one of two voices, either a man's or a woman's. Each has one recorded piece of advice for whoever is in a Citgo at whatever time of night (morning, actually) this is. For future reference, I will call them, respectively, The Man and The Woman. The Man says: if you're hungry, this is the place to go, because they have a varied and extensive selection of salty, sweet, nut-oriented and hot "eats." The Woman says: in case of a "snack attack" this is the place to go, for all the same reasons. I despise The Woman.

Why despise The Woman, you ask?

Hunger is an actual problem. The snack attack is not real. Humans were not born able to feel pain, heat, cold, hunger, and snack attack.

Snack attack is a construct—The Woman an agent of the Simulacrum, the Masonic Great Architect Jahbulon, the dark evil Lovecraftian Underlords of the Market Economy.

The angry reptilian part of me (the part which, after pissing, stands there looking for a few seconds thinking dark half-thought thoughts about former lovers) wants to say this is true of all women. The higher, more reasonable—mammalian—parts of me want to say that these mean thoughts about The Woman are unfair, that the allegations of the reptile-me are untrue, etc.... But fuck 'em—reptile and mammal, lungfish and mole rat—they're not hashing it out on my dime, so the issue remains as it stands: foregrounded but unresolved. Fine. But if The Woman (that is, this woman; not all women) is working on behalf of Dark Forces then The Man must be a member of their special **Applicable** elite unit: a gladiator-cum-archon serving Our Demi-**philosophical** urge of Sparkle and Fade. He dazzles you with colored **lesson: the** packages; with the hope of alleviating a real need—**consumptive** hunger—when it is widely known that no amount of **urge is not** Doritos (cool ranch, extra cheese, fiery ranch, nacho, **related to** guacamole, eXtreme, etc.) or gas station coffee or ten-**the survival** der beef nuggets in foil-wrap (with oxygen-absorbent **instinct.** silica packets to prevent aging) can cure hunger. These things can satiate a snack attack, for illusory desires are best fulfilled by illusory solutions. Thus, if we damn one, we must damn both.... And, if we are issuing sentences, The Man's ring of hell ought by rights to be deeper and hotter and darker. "Buy an extra, for later," The Man's bit concludes. And if I could I would sever his grubby, reaching fingers. The bastards try to get up to the knuckle in your asshole, keep you hooked halfway to the next Citgo.

I do not believe that sitting at this table at this gas station—waiting for the sunrise like a fretful mother waiting for a teenage daughter to stonedly fumble her key into the front door on a given Friday night—will yield up a revelation of any kind. Yet I sit, rolling and smoking cigarettes I neither crave nor want. Why? Because they are there. Drinking Mountain Dew forty-four ounces at a time—I think this is my seventh refill tonight—not because it keeps me going (which it does) but because it is there.

Applicable philosophical lesson: the consumptive urge is not related to the survival instinct.

Likelihood of application in the given scenario: zero.

The clerk wants five minutes to smoke a cigarette of her own. She has long, thin, white ones and I can hear her coughing constantly in the back, but every time she lights one up and starts to tell me the worries of her day (which began at eleven p.m. when the shift started) a rush of customers come in. And customers always need.

These are the directions to the freeway.

We are out of Marlboro 100s.

The bathroom is straight back (I laugh at all the big men, because earlier I masturbated into the men's room toilet. Why? Because it was there.... Take that pronoun however you like.)

I could be bitter.

Earlier she wouldn't give me the fried potato wedges that she was throwing out anyway. She said they tasted bad after a full day under the hot lights, which suggested to me a lack of clarity of communication between herself and myself. Clearly she misjudged the straits I am in, though I cannot imagine how. I have been clear, as clear as a beggar or a bell, and I am clearly hungry—or at least beset by snack attack—and at any rate more or less in need. More in need, at the very least, than the people with working cars and clear destinations, who pour in with clear questions and leave with clear answers and have clear eyes because they aren't sitting here going bloodshot like an old rummy in a cumulus choke of bali shag, floating or treading or considering the prospect of drowning in an endless self-service ocean of warmish sparkling sugars hued like watery electricity. Even if I have, somehow, been less than perfectly clear, there is still our busted van to render the situation lucid.

Our busted van? Well, yeah, I guess I should have said so before, but we are on the way back to Gainesville, Florida, from California.

It is July 26, 2002, and our dirty-orange 1979 VW Microbus blew two tires today after blowing two tires yesterday—the Navajo who replaced our first set of blown tires, it seems, fucked us pretty badly. Us in this scenario is me, my housemates Peter and Adam, this guy Kealan we know and are sort of friends with, who made the trip possible by providing the transportation and doing all the driving (but who, it is worth noting, ran out of money in Tucson [on the way to the coast], when he spent his last $10 on a half-gallon of discount tequila to prepare us for a coming dust storm). And then there's Molly—a fat, friendly, drooly dog with some sort of breathing problem that makes her wheeze all night while we sleep, and sometimes we wake up hearing that bad noise and think Molly is choking to death and we grab for her but she is okay and smiling like dogs do, and drooling on the dirty floor....But this isn't a story about us. This is a story about me, and it takes place while all three men, and the dog, are in the van sleeping.

As I was saying before, these are dire straits that I am in. Nonetheless I have chosen not to be bitter, since the woman (that is, the woman working at the counter here, not Our Lady of the Perpetual Playback Loop: The Woman) meant only to save me from a bad meal I don't need. Instead I hate The Man whose recorded voice convinced me the potato wedges were worth thinking about, worth pursuing, worth desiring—like when the memory of past sex is transformed by your inner reptile to a dream of future sex.

If I were capable of running this Citgo Foodmart I would insist that the clerk take her break. I would do her duties for her, gratis of course. I would insist she smoke two cigarettes. I would insist she smoke ten. My hand and forearm have begun to hurt from writing. Sunrise cannot come soon enough. It feels to me like sunrise may never come. Imagine how the clerk must feel.

The red-and-white checkerboard of the tile on the floor induces a form of madness casually left out of preeminent medical journals— I am thinking especially of the DSM series—and the hour is weird enough that the fact that I've never read a preeminent medical journal bothers me not at all. There are fifty-five bottles of Pennzoil on the top shelf at the back of the aisle closest to me. I can dream worse fates than that of this clerk, but I don't want hers any more for the fact that I want others even less.

Earlier today a prodigiously fat man, wearing sweat shorts held up with suspenders that climbed the seeming acres of his heaving gut (also a green mesh hat and orthopedic tan socks that went up to his knees), said that he used to have a microbus like ours—not just orange either. Blue and purple an' yeller an' flowers too; back before he went into the service. Used to get wasted and sit in the driver's seat, talk about going places but not moving no-where. Hair down to m' ass...back then. I couldn't picture him with hair period. His advice—you want good tires for cheap? Well ya'll get shaved, showered, and new clothes before you go looking. I did not say that if we had all that shit we wouldn't be staying overnight in a Citgo in Fort Smith, Arkansas, for the sake of saving the $50 towing-service charge required by the one place in town that was open when we pulled up at sunset.

> the hour is weird enough that the fact that I've never read a preeminent medical journal bothers me not at all.

I hate the pen I am writing with, but my greatest fear is that it will run out of ink. This pen is the closest thing to the type of pen I prefer that I have seen in weeks. The pens they sell in gas stations are fuck-ing terrible. Fucking jokes is what they are. Fuck Bic, fuck Papermate, fuck souvenir pens hardest. If the pen bears the words GREETINGS FROM, and then the name of the place where you are buying it, it will not work for shit. This is a rule. How much fucking trouble would it fucking be for these fucking Citgo fucking bastards to fucking vend me a fucking black fucking micro-point fucking Uniball with visible fucking inkflow?

A man in a turquoise button shirt with blue suspenders and beige pants gives me a bad look. The clerk says good morning to him. If he says anything to me I'll fucking kill him. I'll take his cock off with my grimy fingernails and use it like a hand puppet. I'll make him talk to it.

Or...maybe I'll pretend to have a drawl and talk to him blandly, pleasantly, about bits of local news I've picked up sitting here. A man was murdered recently, but the clerk didn't know him, which surprised her, because she's lived here a long time.

The man I dreamed briefly of castrating (who was very old, by the way) left some time ago without saying anything to me at all. Nobody says anything to me save the clerk, who (after everyone leaves, even the two fat ladies—one in a blue sweatsuit, one in red) will once again begin to tell me about her day, both of us knowing full well that as soon as she lights up her cigarette and says "I ain't had the chance to fix myself a breakfast sausage yet," a white man or two black men or a white woman with a Spanish man will walk through the door. *What of the restroom?* they will ask. *What of the interstate? What of my snack attack, Goddamnitall?!?*

Men are scum. I know this because I have just used the bathroom and found caked, dried urine on the seat. This since the last time I used the bathroom, merely half of a forty-four ounce Mountain Dew ago. This means the transgression took place in the interim. The possible culprits are few—I suspect the old man in turquoise; this despite the fact that I know he did not even go near the restroom. I have taken care to wipe the seat clean after I use the toilet, in or out of the event of splashing, simply because I respect the clerk who would have to clean my urine if I were not respectful. With a wad of toilet tissue I clean the dried urine of other men, long gone in their automobiles and free of the wrath of my piercing gaze. And how I would glower if they were still here!

After hours of pissing bright yellow, so much that I began to wonder if my body was bothering to metabolize the soda at all, I have just pissed clear. Am I purified then? Of what? Is this some bizarre quirk of the occult or a diet fad waiting to happen? Ought I contact L. Ron Hubbard or Dr. Atkins? Is this worthy of waking up my traveling companions? Of sharing with the clerk, or her less-friendly-seeming coworker who has just arrived? No, I shall keep this to myself until I see how it pans out. There is lots of beer in this store—wine spritzers too—but the clerk and I both know I have nowhere to go drink it but here, and that is against the rules—besides which, I need that money. Perhaps at sunrise I will purchase a single beer to celebrate. If the clerk will allow this, I will purchase two beers and give her the other one. If she will not drink it I will drink them both, having already purchased them and not wanting them to go to waste. All sales final and so on.

A man enters in a grey shirt who resembles my former landlord. It would be amazing if they were relations, but I will not ask and will thus never know, unless I see the former landlord—at a cocktail party, play opening, or elsewhere—and ask him if he has a relation that lives in or might pass through Fort Smith, Arkansas; but even if I see my former landlord, I won't ask. My hand and arm are shot through with pain. I think the pen is winning. If I see the sunrise I will write it down, but I must rest for at least a short time. I know if I want to masturbate again I will need to use the other hand or else risk serious injury. This is not a problem; the other hand will do. Anyway, I don't think I will want to masturbate again. I will finish reading the book I brought with me, I will roll and smoke more cigarettes. Maybe I will talk to the clerk. Maybe I can spare enough money for a potato wedge or a chicken strip. If she puts out fresh ones, juicy inside their newly goldened breading that will appear almost virginal beneath the hot lamp—like the chicken strips were little girls dressed up for first communions—then maybe I will take a chance and trust The Man.

At sunrise there are three employees. The clerk, my clerk, leaves without saying goodbye. The two other clerks do not regard me. It is foggy out. I ask if it is usually foggy out in Arkansas at this time. The short fat clerk says sometimes it is, but other times not. She turns to the thin, pale one who looks vaguely demonic and tells her a story about driving down some road they both know but I do not. The potato wedges and chicken strips are gone. In their places are biscuits with sausages and pigs in blankets that I know to be fresh but do not want. I hate The Man—more than ever. I want a beer more than ever. I refuse to have more soda. I can smell my own body odor, dirt and stale and musk through denim. I need a shower. No! I crave a shower. I need to sleep. But maybe not just yet. The question of where to drink the beer remains.

My forty-four ounce cup is filled with ice. My tongue is stained green from the Mountain Dew. I hurt myself trying to scrape it clean. I will eat some of the ice and wait for the rest to melt. I will eat ice instead of sausage, and I will drink melted ice instead of ice-cold beer. The sky is pink like tender flesh beyond the highway, blue higher up, black nowhere. Anymore.

A flatbed truck carries a bulldozer toward a construction site. In Oklahoma, a barge hit a bridge three months or so before, which is why I-40 is still closed, which is why nobody all night knew where the interstate was (the detour being something on the order of seventy miles), which is also why I got stranded here, in Fort Smith, Arkansas. Here instead of anywhere else, forever and never again. Amen.

Igorot Burial

The Igorots bury their dead with food
wrapped in bark that's chiseled into a canoe.
Attendants say their goodbyes with a chunk
of tilapia, tripe or sticky rice.

> He was a good man   hail mary
> and he liked pork rinds
> Here's a bagful   (praise the lord)

If it were me, I would want friends to eat half
before tucking the bag
crackling under my awful palm.

> It's like going on a picnic at the end of summer.
> I'm the kid in the backseat car ride
> sneaking bits of *adobo* from the basket.

When you think you are probably
dying and the dying is slow
you could obsess over a list of groceries,
dole out responsibilities:

> sister skims aisle nine
> mom fills the cart with leafy greens
> an old friend sticks a dime in the gum machine

Love, if this
is what's happening
I'll wrap ten cases of chocolate bon-bons,
each piece tied with a careful ribbon.

> It works out: you like chocolate.
> I like the word *bon-bons*.

I'm waiting for the numbers and this time
it's not about chicken wings or the next hand.

The results are in the canoe
constructed of jelly I scoop with my fingers.
I'm tempted to swallow every rib and lock socket,
paddles like fish bones lodged in my throat

egg lessons

I.

That woman's a bit runny
at the mouth
every time she exposes
whodunnit. It being something
always being done and annoying that way
like her mouthing off
though she is smart. Despite many accounts

pricking the end of an egg
does not thwart its cracking.
It's a matter of pressure.

In other words
to crack ≠ to prevent cracking

II.

In regards to the matter of
it always being done, don't do it
if it hurts people, as _____'s mother always said. Some advice
is straightforward but sometimes some other

diet gets assigned
and the eggshell can't get strong
if the hen hasn't eaten its share of calcium, manganese, Vitamin D.
They say egg size increases as the hen ages
while the mass of shell stays fixed
which is why big eggs have thin shells which is also why
I hate you.

III.

In the realm of eggs
brown is more expensive. The browner
the bigger and more costly to feed.
Is there anything more elegant

than a hard boiled egg coming undone?
Breakfast eggcellence.

IV.
Into the trash the empty carton thumped. This morning I gulped
what juice was left, fried the last two eggs, griddled the leftover batter—
I said goddamit everything is always running out, and Mike

laughed at me which was
appropriate and I considered
writing a poem titled "eggsistential: a love poem"
but what good would come out of that

CIRCUS

:: by Terry Dalrymple ::

Folks in Phlattsland, Texas, referred to the Macks as "that queer bunch out on the county line." Some said their life was a circus. Like that youngest boy, Millard, they said, born on the kitchen table while the family ate supper.

Millard Mack was born, in fact, not on the kitchen table but on the kitchen floor of a rattletrap frame house eleven miles north of Phlattsland, Texas. He came late to the Macks. When he slid from his mother's womb onto the kitchen floor, his brothers were thirteen and fifteen. Millard's mother, Delia Mack, six-foot-two and just shy of 300 pounds, stood in the kitchen preparing a lunch of sausage and cabbage when she felt the first contraction. Gaylord and the teenage boys were out sowing cotton seed, but she felt no urgency to alert them. These things took time, she knew. But Millard apparently did not know. Within minutes the contractions were frequent and intense—so intense, in fact, that she collapsed by the stove. When her water broke she summoned the wherewithal to bunch her huge skirt up around her waist and shove her underwear far enough down her legs that she could squirm and wriggle and kick them off. Two contractions later she bore down and, as she later told her sister on the phone, "shot that little darlin' halfway to the 'firdgerator."

Afterwards, she wrapped Millard in a fold of her skirt and felt around on the counter above her until her hand found the cabbage-cutting knife. She sliced the umbilical cord, tied it off, and back-slapped the mucus out of him. By the time Gaylord and the teenage boys tromped in for lunch, she had propped her back against the stove and bared her breasts for Millard's first meal.

Gaylord Mack, six-foot-six and skinny as a cotton stalk, stood just inside the kitchen, wrinkling his nose at the mess Millard's birth had made on the floor. The two boys stood behind him, their mouths agape. Siefert, the older boy, stood head-to-head with his father and only a few pounds heavier. Cantrell was an inch shorter but already tended toward his mother's weightiness.

Millard Mack turned four exactly eight days before his oldest brother, Siefert, ran over himself with a tractor.

After a long and silent survey, Cantrell spoke first: "I'm hungry, Mama."

"Yeah," his brother agreed. "We're starved."

"Shut up," Gaylord snapped. "You boys go on, now, and quit starin' at your mama's titties." The boys grumbled but shuffled out of the kitchen.

Delia quivered, and her voice was weak. "We got to get to San Angelo," she said. "To the hospital."

Gaylord shoved his big hands into his overalls pockets and shrugged. "What for? It's already borned." He studied his wife's flushed cheeks, wisps of long straight hair clinging to them damply. "Anyways," he said, "you don't look so bad."

Delia's voice trembled. "For the baby," she said. "For your new baby boy."

His eyes shifted to the wrinkled ball of flesh squirming at one of Delia's large sagging breasts. He pointed at the infant with his chin. "He's suckin', ain't he? I reckon he's okay."

Folks in Phlattsland, Texas, referred to the Macks as "that queer bunch out on the county line." Like circus clowns, they said. Like that oldest boy, Siefert, they said, who ran over himself with a tractor. Or the middle one, Cantrell, they said, queer in more ways than one, that boy who fell naked from a roof and broke his neck. And in fact, though their details were hazy, they were right about the deaths.

Millard Mack turned four exactly eight days before his oldest brother, Siefert, ran over himself with a tractor. Like his father, Siefert was silent and sullen. Still, he had found a girl, one who preferred action to conversation. One night, frustrated because his father denied him access to the family's only vehicle—a ten-year-old Ford pickup truck—Siefert stole his father's tractor, older than the truck, and drove nine miles with no lights to visit Linda Slocum. Linda smuggled a fifth of her daddy's Jack Daniels and the two of them lay naked on a blanket in the middle of a cotton field, drinking and making love until dawn. On his way home, drunk and exhausted, Siefert toppled off the tractor seat and a back tire crushed his skull.

After the funeral, Gaylord and Cantrell Mack spent the afternoon in the barn repairing the tractor, damaged from flipping onto its side twenty yards from Siefert's crushed skull. Delia Mack sat on the kitchen floor and leaned against the stove. She buried little Millard's head against her huge breasts and wept until her husband and older son returned to the house for supper.

Two years later, Cantrell fell off Danny Piestrowsky's roof and broke his neck. He was naked at the time. One of Linda Slocum's many cousins, Danny claimed that with his parents out of town he and Cantrell had taken two girls onto the roof to drink beer and watch the stars. He refused to name the girls, and none ever confessed. Some folks speculated it had been the Mattingly twins, a wild pair who a year later both turned up pregnant by the same man, a thirty-two-year-old farm-implements salesman from San Angelo. Others believed there had been no girls at all and that Danny, too, had been naked when Cantrell plunged to his death.

When the sheriff called, Gaylord Mack went alone to the scene of the accident. Delia, sobbing, awakened Millard and led him by the hand into the kitchen.

Folks in Phlattsland, Texas, referred to the Macks as "that queer bunch out on the county line." They belong in a circus, they said. Like that crazy one, Delia, they said, the one who died painting a horse. And Delia had, in fact, painted a horse, but she died after, not during, the task.

"A dwarf, honey," *Delia said. "Or a* *midget. Whichever."* *Millard reached* *across her shoulder* *and touched the* *page. "Wisht I was* *tiny," Delia said* *wistfully.*

Millard was sixteen at the time. By then, he stood six-foot-seven and had grudgingly assumed responsibility for most of the farming work. He attended school most days, but remained aloof and had no friends. He rarely spoke, except when his father slept and he and his mother sat at the kitchen table playing double solitaire, he spitting snuff into a Coke can, she sipping Gallo red.

One Friday evening he ambled into the kitchen expecting to find, as usual, the cards laid out and his mother waiting quietly, her hands folded on the table in front of her. Instead, her hands lay flat along the edges of a magazine, and she smiled wistfully at the open pages. Millard retrieved two tattered decks of cards from a drawer near the sink and sat opposite his mother. He set the red deck near the top of the magazine and began shuffling the blue deck. His mother neither turned pages nor looked up nor spoke.

Millard began laying out a row of seven cards. "What is it, Mama?"

"Life," she said, still smiling softly. *"Life* magazine."

He set his remaining cards in the middle of the table, careful to avoid a sticky spot of honey dribbled there. "You playin'?"

"Come around here, Mill. Look at this."

He cast a critical eye over his up-cards, then shoved out his chair, stood, and walked around to look over her shoulder. "It's a circus," she said. "Wisht I could go to a circus." The color photograph spread across both pages and appeared to be taken from atop the tent's center pole. In the foreground, a man in shiny blue tights hung by his knees on a suspended bar and gripped the arms of a woman in matching tights who dangled beneath him. Below, all three rings were visible. In one, five jugglers tossed fifteen flaming batons. In the middle ring, five solid white horses galloped in a circle, each with a different colored shimmering blanket across its back, on which stood a performer in a sequined outfit that matched the blanket. The third ring encircled four clowns chasing another who drove a car far too small for him. A huge crowd watched from the stands.

"Look here," said Millard's mother. She pointed with a long fat finger to what appeared to be a little girl standing on one of the white horses. "It says her name's Minnie." She licked her forefinger and turned the page. "That's her."

The left-hand page contained a close-up of Minnie, who grinned broadly and curtsied from atop her white horse. Her pink sequined dress sparkled brilliantly. Millard's mouth dropped open. "That ain't no little girl."

Delia chuckled softly. "A woman," she said.

"She's so tiny, Mama."

"A dwarf, honey," Delia said. "Or a midget. Whichever." Millard reached across her shoulder and touched the page. "Wisht I was tiny," Delia said wistfully.

Millard traced the little woman's figure with one finger. "A dwarf," he said.

"Wisht we could go to the circus," Delia dreamily mused.

"Or a midget," Millard said. His finger came to rest on Minnie's shoulder. "Whichever." They remained silent for a time, staring at the picture. "Can I have it, Mama?" Millard finally asked. "Can I have this pitcher?"

"When I'm done, sweetie." She patted his hand. "You go on to bed now. No cards tonight, okay?"

Millard gathered the cards and returned them to their drawer. "Don't forget, Mama," he said before leaving the kitchen. "Don't forget to give me that pitcher."

"Wisht I was tiny," Delia said.

Two hours later she stumbled into Millard's room and shook him awake. She set the picture, carefully cut from the magazine, on his chest. "Don't muss it," she slurred, her breath thick with Gallo red. "Keep it good." Then she stumbled out.

Millard arose and gently tacked the page on the wall facing his bed. He lay staring at it for over an hour, his feet sticking off the end of his too-short bed. "A dwarf," he said when he finally turned off the light. "Or a midget. Whichever."

The next morning, they found Delia's body outside in a faded pink housedress. She had painted their old sorrel nag white and died of a heart attack trying to mount it.

Folks in Phlattsland, Texas, referred to the Macks as "that queer pair, father and son, out on the county line." Goofy as circus clowns, they said. Like the father, Gaylord, they said, who ran away from home and left a seventeen-year-old boy to run the cotton farm. And in this, they were right, though they didn't know that Millard Mack later held a shotgun to his head or that Linda Slocum propositioned him.

Six months after burying Delia, Gaylord Mack walked into the kitchen one morning carrying a battered suitcase in one hand and two threadbare blankets under his other arm. Millard sat at the table eating toast and honey.

"I'm leavin'," Gaylord said.

Millard did not look at him. He swallowed a bite of toast, then asked, "Where to?"

"Find me a wife."

"You got one."

"Dead one. Man needs a live wife."

Millard dropped the remaining toast onto his plate. "You go to hell."

Gaylord turned and strolled toward the front door. "Reckon I'll see you there, 'less I get back before then." In fact, he would never come back.

Millard took the elder Mack's twenty-gauge shotgun and walked to the middle of their cotton field. He sat cross-legged between rows and pushed the barrel up under his chin. He sat there until dark, then returned the shotgun, untacked the picture of Minnie from his wall, and carried it with him out to the road. He walked halfway to Phlattsland before Linda Slocum, returning from a weekend trip to Dallas, pulled up beside him.

"You want a ride, Millard Mack?" she asked. He folded his tall frame into her Camaro and they drove a mile or so in silence before Linda, who had been drinking, said, "Where you going?"

"Anywheres."

"Your daddy know?"

"Ain't got no daddy."

Linda slowed, steered onto the grassy shoulder, and turned off the engine. She pulled a flask out of her purse, took a swig, and held it out to Millard. "Drink with me," she said.

"Don't drink," Millard replied.

"What are you, Baptist or something?"

"Wouldn't know," Millard said.

Linda shrugged and took another long swig. "Your brother drank. It's what killed him, I guess. Or maybe I did." The whisky was working, and her voice turned melancholy. "It was my idea, you know. Siefert sneaking out that night. Going to that cotton field. Drinking and making love. It was all my idea." She paused for another drink. Millard remained silent, hunched in the seat so his head wouldn't hit the roof of the car. She drained the flask and returned it to her purse. Then she turned on the dome light, cupped Millard's chin in her hand, and turned his face toward her. "You look a lot like him," she said. "Come with me out in that field." She pointed out the window to the barely visible cotton field.

Millard shook his head. "No thanks."

"No thanks! Are you queer or something? Everybody wants me. Nobody says no thanks."

"I ain't queer."

"They don't say just plain thanks, either. They might say please, but never thanks."

Folks in Phlattsland, Texas, referred to Millard Mack as "that queer fellow out on the county line." Running off to the circus at twenty-two, they said, like a little boy in a movie.

"I ain't no queer." He opened the car door, ducked his head to exit, but she grabbed his arm.

"Don't," she said. He hesitated long enough to look back, saw the tears wetting her cheeks, looked back out into the darkness. "I'm twenty-nine, Millard Mack. Folks say I'm beautiful and shake their heads because I'm not married." She wiped at the tears with the back of her hand. "He's the only one. Your brother Siefert is the only one who's ever said thanks." She pulled her auburn hair into a ponytail, then let it fall back over her shoulders. She patted his arm. "Never mind," she said. She wiped her eyes, puffed her cheeks, and exhaled audibly. "Do you need money, Millard Mack?"

"I ain't got none."

"You should stay," she said. "I'll help. You should stay on the farm."

"Thanks," he said.

Folks in Phlattsland, Texas, referred to Millard Mack as "that queer fellow out on the county line." Running off to the circus at twenty-two, they said, like a little boy in a movie. And Millard Mack did, in fact, run off to the circus when he was twenty-two. But he would return.

His meager crop harvested, he packed a few belongings into the old truck he had bought with a loan from Linda Slocum five years earlier. As he pumped gas into it at Slocum's Gas and Garage, owned by Linda's father, Linda stepped out of the little hamburger grill next door, also owned by her father. "I'm getting married, Millard Mack."

"Reckon that's good," Millard said as he replaced his gas cap.

"It is. Colby Bartlett. He says thanks. Always. Every time." She spotted the little suitcase on his passenger side seat. "Where are you going?"

"Circus," he said, heading inside to pay for his gas.

She frowned. "There's no circus around here."

"Reckon not," Millard replied. "But there's got to be one somewheres." He paid, returned to his truck, and headed west.

A month and a half later he strolled into Linda Bartlett nee Slocum's wedding reception. He held himself straight and looked down directly into people's eyes. They gawked and fell silent as he passed, shocked not so much to see him as to see the tiny woman who scurried along next to him. The top of her head did not even reach his waist. In the middle of the reception hall, he slipped his hands into the small woman's armpits and lifted her above his head. Her tiny feet dangled in front of his face. Linda Bartlett née Slocum stood directly in front of them wearing an unconventional wedding dress, a short, skin-tight little number with a plunging neck line.

"This here's Teensy," Millard Mack announced. He turned a slow circle so that everyone could see her. She smiled and waved her miniature hand. "She's a midget," Millard said, "not a dwarf. And she's my wife." He raised his voice to be heard over the low murmur that had begun among the reception guests. "I ain't queer," he said. He set Teensy gently back on her feet and spoke again, this time more quietly: "I ain't no queer." Then he and Teensy exited the room and drove toward his ramshackle frame house eleven miles north of Phlattsland, Texas.

Folks in Phlattsland, Texas, referred to the Macks as "that queer couple out on the county line." Circus freaks, they said. A giant and a dwarf, they said. Ruined Linda Bartlett née Slocum's wedding reception, many said. Aside from Linda's dress, some men said, they provided the best entertainment of the day. It didn't matter, some women said, because at thirty-four Linda Slocum had no business holding a big wedding anyway. A circus, they said. A veritable circus.

Cherry Blossoms, Blue Mountain, Chickadee
by John Repp

Good to be home from Kentucky,
to sprawl in my chair's quilted hand,
to rest my eyes on the things we've arranged

for the six months before we ferry them elsewhere.
Good not to eat lasagna at the Haymarket Restaurant
as two men curse the Ohio Navy, the overpass proclaiming

Rusty Loves Lisa Luke Stay Away in metallic blue.
Good not to search for gas near Charleston,
not to hear three monarch butterflies

smash into the windshield as I glide to a stop,
not to see omen in the beautiful death,
a self thinking itself the center of things

at a Gulf station with one working toilet.
I wiped the glass clean of gore and wings, got my gas
and drove away from the swelter of Kentucky,

away from Baptist churches and gun shops by the horde,
away from sausage gravy and biscuits and the charred
remains of the haunch or belly or shoulder or cloven hoof

of the holy pig. I hauled my galvanized tub of disdain
home to our fake ivory Shiva devouring
and birthing generations while lentil soup simmers.

I look at the prints Jim bought in Shanghai.
I look through the box scores and the mail.
I watch you talk on the phone.

My black-glass heart mirrors you.

:: by Ellen Morris Prewitt ::

Godzilla vs. The Code

My husband has a favorite Japanese actor, and he can pronounce the man's name. *To-shi-ro Mi-fu-ne.* At our house, Mr. Mifune appears in Samurai movies, mostly on Saturday afternoons. I'll walk into the TV room and there's my husband on the couch, reading subtitles. The men on TV are dressed in black, they huff out their lines.

I cannot make fun of my husband.

My favorite Japanese actor is Godzilla.

In the Samurai movies, the men have a Code. I don't understand the Code but it seems very important. For one thing, the men bow, then die over the Code often. For another, the movies are shot in black and white and that makes anything seem important.

Godzilla, on the other hand, has no Code. He isn't even Good or Bad. Sometimes at the beginning of a movie he's Good and later in the same move, he becomes Bad. In one movie he's saving Tokyo. The next time you see him, he's spewing radioactive fire across the city's rooftops. Void of agenda, directionless, virtually without plot, the monster rampages.

Those of you who know Mr. Mifune's work may object to my discussing his film career in the same breath as that of Godzilla. But your offense would be misguided. Just as Mr. Mifune embodied the essence of the Japanese tateyaku style of acting, so did Godzilla embody the essence of post-World War II Japan. That is, he did until he became kitsch.

Wait, you say. Godzilla was always kitsch.

No, he wasn't. Look back before the Godzilla directors became enamored with space aliens. In the first movie, filmed in 1954 by Tomoyuki Tanaka (*Gojira*), you see the cinematic image of the only people instructed in the horrors of the nuclear bomb. Godzilla's early monsterography confirms this view: Godzilla was awakened by the Allied dropping of the atomic bomb on Japan, the monster rising from the sea as an inexplicable, chaotic force, one totally owned within the Japanese experience.

Later, as happens with so many who become famous, Godzilla's backstory changed. Under the revised version, Godzilla becomes a mutant created by irresponsible American nuclear testing on an atoll. In these movies, the Japanese people quit examining their own experience and looked outward. Godzilla—he who once represented the unthinkable—is reduced to the lesser, and more boring, political.

I admire the early Godzilla in part because he has no Code. He doesn't follow the Code of the Samurais, the Code trumpeted by Ernest Hemingway and other testosterone-saturated writers. The Code does nothing for me. In fact, when I read Hemingway, I wonder, who decided this was good? The Code as enacted by the Samurai is somewhat less off-putting, probably because it's in Japanese and I don't understand it as well. But the Code that treats men like pawns on the chessboard, tabs in the computer chip, rats in the maze — I am not a fan.

I prefer the chaos of Godzilla.

Godzilla, being what he is, appears on the TV screen at our house mostly at night. In the afternoon, we loll in front of the Samurai matinee; at night, we tense to the true Godzilla. We watch with the Japanese people as they scan the horizon for the lumbering monster. Suddenly, he stomps onto the screen — a collective, national night-terror, a post-traumatic stress creature destined to die, and boil anew when the camera cranks again. The creature's sole purpose: to rise without ceasing or resolve. Like an open, cinematic wound, *Godzilla!* erupts.

THE ILLUSTRATED STORY

In each issue of Barrelhouse, we ask an artist to interpret and adapt one of the stories from our website. This issue includes "Sex and Pills: A Love Story," an original story by Carrie Hill Wilner, here adapted by artist and photographer Kylos Brannon.

SEX & PILLS
A LOVE STORY

CAST:
Jupiter Sauter
Josh Limbaugh
Denman Anderson
Jessica Rudman

FROM THE ARTIST:
Special thanks to Kimberly Klinger and Jessica Rudman. Kim shot the photos I was in for Sex/Pills and Jess was nice enough to make out with me for it and get in the shower for Like A Mexican. She risked having her butt in the magazine. That's the sign of a good girlfriend.

WELLBUTRIN SR 150MG TAB GLAX

It's not like
I wanted
to think about
sex more often.
My libido was the only
thing about me that had always
been healthy.

more like intrusive

OPEN

PUSH DOWN & TURN

CLOSE

"Carrie,
one I'm-thinking-
about-fucking-you-
on-the-desk
voicemail a day
is really enough."

"Is it?"

"Yeah."
"Oh sorry."

I first went on brain candy to fix the fact that I was a fucked-up kid,
**hoped I'd benefit from the drugs' legendary side effect
of lessened sexual desire.**
Maybe I'd be able to get some work done

SWALLOW WHOLE
DO NOT CRUSH
OR CHEW

I went through just about every SSRI there was,
trying to find one that didn't give me nightmares
or make me throw up.

BUPROPION
This medicine is
an antidepressant

But my sexual desire -
never distinct from "desire"
in general, in my mind
- remained unthwarted.

it's not like sex was that great.

I didn't know
what I was doing,
and neither did the
bartenders and
shy boyfriends who peopled my adolescence.

Like Paoulo In Milan

**i was quite literally homeless
moved in with him for a bit**
was eating his food
and wearing his shirts
and i didnt know anyone
and had nothing to do

"Sweetie, when are you coming home?
Carlo's coming over?   Shit.....
When's he coming?
With you?
Well, when's he leaving?
Yes I'll pick up the wine and start
the water boiling."

the wine bought and the pasta thrown in,
fifteen minutes before they walked in the door
I'd sit on the floor
with a coffee mug of chianti
and try to watch the news

his skin on parts of my arms
that I knew touched his chest
when I wrapped them around him

TAKE OR USE THIS EXACTLY
AS DIRECTED.
DO NOT SKIP DOSES
OR DISCONTINUE

THE SMELL
of his soap and latex

my toes would curl

my palms turn red and warm

us and Carlo, for chrissake,
who, actually wasn't half bad
but he wasn't the reason
I was drumming my fingers
impatiently

and I want

i want i want

i want
i want
i want
i want

Anticipation
out of proportion
to the satisfaction

When Carlo left,
a glance was enough
to send Paulo to the bathroom
for the condoms and
we'd fuck on the linoleum floor
where I'd been sitting alone
two hours before and it was...
okay.

Conceptually, with the sweat and the bodies
and whatever, it was all there, but if sweat and bodies
were all I was after, I could have gone to the gym.

the pill-hopping went on for a while
and got me nowhere -
still throwing up and having nightmares,
still being a fucked-up kid,
as in mostly I cried a lot.
I was, according to various sources,
moping, insane,
scared,
manifesting allergies
in strange ways,
scary, tired, a
victim of my times,
of bourgeois
malaise,
of a total lack
of self-control.

I took **Prozac Paxil,** Zoloft, **LUVOX** and **Effexor.**

None of which is advertised as a cure for bourgeois malaise.

No wonder they didn't work.

"Let's add Wellbutrin to your regimen. It ups dopamine, it's a bit of a stimulant."

READ THE PATIENT INFORMATION LEAFLET THAT CAME WITH THIS MEDICINE

If it's called **Wellbutrin,** it can't be bad right?

all the other stuff

sex

So I started taking these purple-grey pills. I'm less tired.

Despite a Pac-man shaped wedge of my mental pie chart being devoted to sex

It had not been:

bolts of
**electric
liquor**
pop rocks
**surging
up
my
spine**
synaptic shocks
**down every
nerve**
like I'd kicked the radio
into the tub
like you warn
curious children to never
ever do **finishing
flushed
and
dazed**
hands shaking

Yeah.

That good.

Every time.

where am I and what the fuck is that?

It's not just transcendental orgasm that comes courtesy of my new favorite pill
I'm happier
not placid-tired-zen-**happy**
DO NOT DRINK ALCOHOLIC BEVERAGES WHILE TAKING THIS MEDICINE
sex
chomp
chomp
chomp
but make-that-a-**Makers-on-the-rocks**-damn-I-look-good-in-these-jeans-**do-you-dare-me-to? happy**. Confident, even.

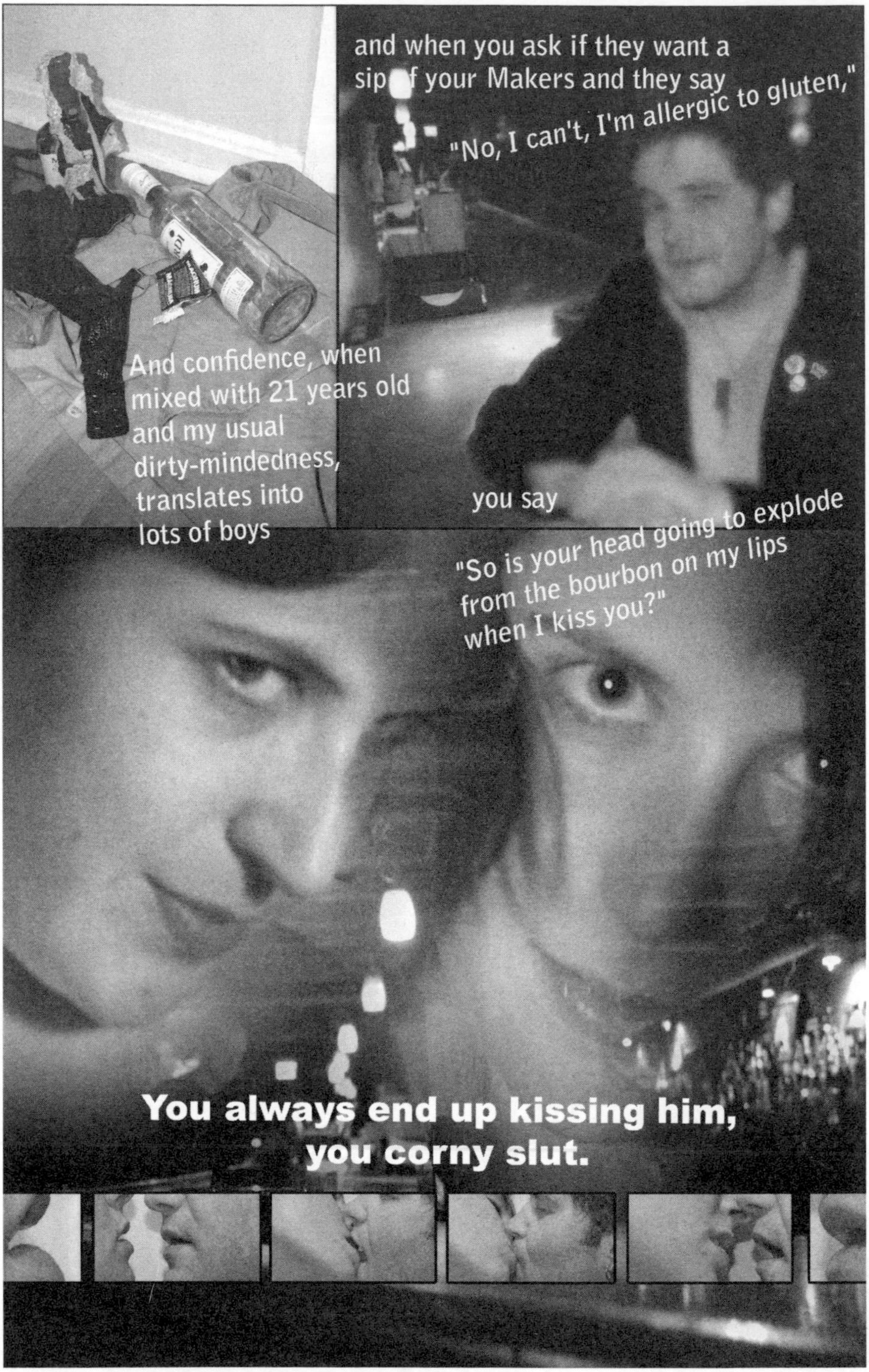
and when you ask if they want a
sip f your Makers and they say
"No, I can't, I'm allergic to gluten,"
And confidence, when
mixed with 21 years old
and my usual
dirty-mindedness,
translates into
lots of boys
you say
"So is your head going to explode
from the bourbon on my lips
when I kiss you?"
You always end up kissing him,
you corny slut.

And then when you're making him a four a.m. cup of tea

back at your place and he slips his arm around your waist

and it startles you and you spill boiling water on your hand

you almost do it right there against the fridge but your roommate comes in

and it turns red instantly and he's so sorry and is getting you a paper towel with cold water on it

but there's no anesthetic better than your scalded hand on the small of his back

and your tongue in his mouth, there's no pain because your nerves have lost all discretion,

turning every sen-sation into high voltage ichor

back in your bed it's ridiculous how many times you come, like at least four and it's not like you're fucking for more than a few minutes and afterwards he says, "Damn, not that I questioned my abilities..." because he's a little bit cocky "... but I've never been with anyone who made me feel like I was that good."

And you say It's not you, it's me.

one morning I wake up in an apartment next to someone good-looking
who I'm glad I didn't fuck

MAY CAUSE NAUSEA
just leave him
sleeping
and take
painfully
slow cab
ride

just because I can do this every weekend
doesn't mean I have to.
Not that I can think of a
good reason to stop.

And I tell the shrinkwrapper that ever
since I've been on these pills I've been
like a brash sexual superhero, which is a
lot of responsibility for one little girl
and she says, well, yes, it's entirely possible
that the drug could be making you a bit manic
and we both sort of nod and then I tell her
something about my thesis because I'd rather
talk about that. **REFILLS 3 QTY 60**
TELEPHONE AHEAD FOR FASTER REFILLS

If you've been paying attention,

you've no doubt noticed that we here at Barrelhouse have a little bit of a thing for pop culture. Maybe you'd call that thing an obsession, but we prefer to think of it as a totally healthy devotion, even love. You could say, in fact, that Barrelhouse is a sort of love letter to pop culture, or even a shrine. A shrine in the metaphorical sense, of course.

But why stop, we asked, at the level of metaphor? If something's worth doing, is it not also worth overdoing? Why not build a physical shrine, the sort of thing we could offer up to the gods of pop culture and beseech them to shower us with their good favor? Why not build an altar at which we could pray for the gods to rain down their blessings upon us? Maybe one more KISS reunion and one less Rolling Stones Superbowl half-time performance? Could the pop culture gods make *The O.C.* funny again? Can we get some more Mr. T in our lives?

To build our shrine we raided our closets and our bookcases, our eighth grade record collections and the crap we'd stuffed into boxes and crammed into the corners of our basements. We unearthed trading cards and figurines and things we'd rather not own up to still owning (because love, as we all know, is not really love unless you love the bad parts along with the good). It's all here, in the Barrelhouse Shrine to Pop Culture. Behold, the magical geekiness that is Barrelhouse.

From left, kind of back to front and then moving again to the left:

Phil Collins *Face Value* LP

Spongebob Squarepants sippy cup

Bob's Big Boy rubber coin bank

Dan Akroyd autographed picture

Bob and Doug McKenzie *Great White North* LP

Duran Duran *Rio* single

Antique clown coin bank

Ralph Ellison *Invisible Man* book

Superman book

C3PO Star Wars trading card

Skull drinking mug

Bulleit Frontier Whiskey bottle

Ukulele

Complete book of M.A.S.H.

Scary Pinocchio marionette

Loverboy *Get Lucky* LP

Buddy Jesus

Matryoshka Doll

Star Wars thermos

Yukon Cornelius figurine

Manute Bol NBA trading card

Small pink clay dog

Aimee Bender *The Girl in the Flammable Skirt* book

Better Off Dead videotape

Lance Bass bobblehead

Superman mug

iPod mini

Fake skull crap

Transformer

Morrissey *You Are the Quarry* postcard

Lava lamp

Maker's Mark Kentucky Bourbon bottle

Tony Hawk's Underground X-box game

Thomas Jones *Sonny Liston Was a Friend of Mine* book

Spawn figurine

Creepy mask

Clash Combat Rock LP

Toto "Toto IV" LP

Donnie Darko *Why Are You Wearing that Stupid Man Suit* postcard

Above:

Bill Murray in *Ghostbusters* photo

Marie Leveau Voodoo packet

Photo of pug wearing baseball hat

How Cheap Can You Get pulp novel postcard

Voodoo doll

Red Hot Creole Pepper Sauce sign

Gene Simmons KISS card

Buddha statue

Paul Stanley KISS card

Yankees kids size baseball hat

Name tag: "Katie"

CONTRIBUTORS

BRIAN AMES writes from St. Charles County, Missouri. His work appears in several magazines, including *North American Review, Glimmer Train, The Massachusetts Review,* and *Night Train.* He is the author of the story collections *Smoke Follows Beauty* (Pocol Press, 2002), *Head Full of Traffic* (Pocol Press, 2004), and *Eighty-Sixed* (Word Riot Press, 2004). He is a fiction editor at *Word Riot,* and a former editor of *Wind Row,* Washington State University's literary journal.

SEAN BEAUDOIN lives in San Francisco with his wife Cathy and daughter Stella. Additional stories will appear in coming issues of *Glimmer Train, The New Orleans Review,* and *Fugue.* His novel, *Going Nowhere Faster,* will be published by Little, Brown in Fall 2006. He can be contacted at: Headsnap@aol.com.

MATT BELL is a fiction writer and poet living in Saginaw, Michigan. His writing has appeared in many fine literary magazines, including *Hobart, The Driftwood Review, The Drexel Online Journal, Cellar Door,* and *Me Three.*

ILANA BOIVIE has, in twenty-six years, lived on three of seven continents and endured the affections of one Barrelhouse editor. When not copyediting, she takes classes in economics and calculus.

KYLOS BRANNON makes pretty pictures, sometimes they move, sometimes they tell a story, a few have been featured in some short film festivals, and some are in documentaries produced by Hillmann & Carr, Inc., and featured in museums around the country. Kylos teaches at George Washington University's Art Department and American University's School of Communication, helping others to make pretty pictures. He works with Barrelhouse producing Take That Hill, a night of short films and readings... look for it to come to a town near you (if you live in D.C. or Pennsylvania). You can reach him at www.mistermayhem.com/kylos.

TERRY DALRYMPLE teaches English at Angelo State University, a regional university in San Angelo, Texas. His publications include *Salvation,* a book of short fiction published by Panther Creek Press, and *Fishing for Trouble,* a novel for middle readers published by New Win Publishing.

TIM HALL is a book designer in Brooklyn who occasionally defends our land from swarthy communists. Wolverines forever!

LEENA JAYASWAL is an assistant professor at American University's School of Communication, a photographer, and an independent documentary filmmaker. The photo she contributed to this issue was shot during the production of *Dischord Records: An Impression*, a documentary about Ian MacKaye's record label produced by Leena and Kylos Brannon.

LEE KLEIN edits Eyeshot.net and lives in Iowa City, where he's learning how to write fiction along with one of the Barrelhouse editors.

DAVE LONGAKER is a salesman, cooler, and philosopher living in Washington, D.C. He dances poorly, knows no martial art, and doesn't feel one way or the other about children or the elderly. He is currently doing background research for new work that takes inspiration from the events depicted in *Hot Dog: The Movie*.

ANASTASIA MILLER is a designer and—after a life-changing trip to Ukraine this fall—aspiring photojournalist who lives with her husband and daughter in Washington, D.C. She works as the creative director for the Peace Corps.

PAULA MORRIS is a New Zealand writer who lives (hurricanes and floods permitting) in New Orleans. She is the author of two novels, *Queen of Beauty* and *Hibiscus Coast*, both published by Penguin Books New Zealand, and teaches at Tulane University.

ELLEN MORRIS PREWITT lives with her husband on an island in the Mississippi River. A plastic Godzilla roars, mouth open, on her bed stand.

DERRICK S. PILE is twenty-four, has been previously published in the journal *Slipstream*, and wants to thank his mother and father for all their support. Currently a bank teller, Derrick would like to find another job, preferably one that will showcase his incredible editing ability.

JOHN REPP's third full-length collection of poetry, *Gratitude*, was published in autumn 2005 by Cherry Grove Collections.

KAREN SCHOENHALS is a national award-winning poet. She received a bachelor of arts degree in creative writing from Northwestern University. Her poems have appeared in *Rattle, Louisiana Literature, Blue Unicorn, The William and Mary Review, The Louisville Review, Nightsun, Lullwater Review,* and *New Millennium Writings.* In 1997 she was the recipient of the national New Millennium Poetry Award. She is a professional classical guitarist and lives in South Florida.

NANCY SLAVIN received her master's degree in English from Portland State University and she currently works as a creative writing instructor as well as a non-violence educator for a small non-profit. She's published two chapbooks of poetry, *The Nature of Gratitude* and *Public Access,* both of which are influenced by the beauty of the Oregon coast, where she lives with her family.

THERESA SOTTO lives in Santa Monica, California, where she works as a freelance writer. Her poetry has appeared or will be appearing in *ZYZZYVA, Spinning Jenny,* and *Cartographica.*

JUSTIN TAYLOR is a freelance writer of fiction, journalism, poetry, and "other." His work has appeared in—or on the websites of—*The Nation, Punk Planet, Rain Taxi, The Brooklyn Rail,* and elsewhere. He is based out of New York City and is an MFA candidate at The New School. Visit his complete, evolving archive of published works at www.justindtaylor.net

TOM WILLIAMS edits *Arkansas Review: A Journal of Delta Studies* (www.clt.astate.edu/arkreview) and teaches at Arkansas State University. His short fiction is forthcoming in *Boulevard* and *Connecticut Review* and has appeared in such journals as *Night Train, Indiana Review,* and *River City.*

CARRIE HILL WILNER lives in New York City and is a regular contributor, former editor, columnist for *Nerve.* She is currently working on her first novel.

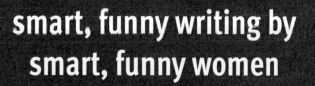

POET
LORE
Established 1889

Read the oldest continually published poetry journal in the U.S

From cover of Spring 2005 issue

Subscribe today:
visit www.writer.org

FROM THE
TO THE

For more Barrelhousey goodness, visit our website. What'll you find there? We're so glad you asked:

Original fiction, updated all the time

Essays, reviews, and the rantings of people who take pop culture way too seriously

Interviews with people who are way cooler than us

Subscription information

Submission guidelines

The Literary Dodgeball Challenge (duck!)

The Barrelhouse Buzz, the little e-mail list that could...or can...or just might, someday, if it ever got off its ass and got its shit together

...and more Barrelhousey goodness.

Okay, so we just like saying "Barrelhousey goodness."

www.barrelhousemag.com